SYMBIOSIS

THE PEARSON CUSTOM LIBRARY FOR THE
BIOLOGICAL SCIENCES

Pearson Learning Solutions

New York   Boston   San Francisco
London   Toronto   Sydney   Tokyo   Singapore   Madrid
Mexico City   Munich   Paris   Cape Town   Hong Kong   Montreal

D1360225

Senior Vice President, Editorial and Marketing: Patrick F. Boles
Senior Sponsoring Editor: Natalie Danner
Development Editor: Annette Fantasia
Assistant Editor: Jill Johnson
Executive Marketing Manager: Nathan L. Wilbur
Operations Manager: Eric M. Kenney
Production Manager: Jennifer Berry
Art Director: Renée Sartell
Cover Designer: Kristen Kiley

Cover Art: Courtesy of Michael R. Martin, Darryl Johnson, Photodisk, DK Images, and Prentice-Hall, Inc.

This special edition published in cooperation with Pearson Learning Solutions.

Printed in the United States of America.

V092

Please visit our web site at *www.pearsoncustom.com.*

Attention bookstores: For permission to return unused stock, contact us at *pe-uscustomreturns@pearson.com.*

Pearson Learning Solutions, 501 Boylston Street, Suite 900, Boston, MA 02116
A Pearson Education Company
www.pearsoned.com

ISBN 10: 1-256-19412-3
ISBN 13: 978-1-256-19412-5

Laboratory Safety: General Guidelines

1. Notify your instructor immediately if you are pregnant, color blind, allergic to any insects or chemicals, taking immunosuppressive drugs, or have any other medical condition (such as diabetes, immunologic defect) that may require special precautionary measures in the laboratory.

2. Upon entering the laboratory, place all books, coats, purses, backpacks, etc. in designated areas, not on the bench tops.

3. Locate and, when appropriate, learn to use exits, fire extinguisher, fire blanket, chemical shower, eyewash, first aid kit, broken glass container, and cleanup materials for spills.

4. In case of fire, evacuate the room and assemble outside the building.

5. Do not eat, drink, smoke, or apply cosmetics in the laboratory.

6. Confine long hair, loose clothing, and dangling jewelry.

7. Wear shoes at all times in the laboratory.

8. Cover any cuts or scrapes with a sterile, waterproof bandage before attending lab.

9. Wear eye protection when working with chemicals.

10. Never pipet by mouth. Use mechanical pipeting devices.

11. Wash skin immediately and thoroughly if contaminated by chemicals or microorganisms.

12. Do not perform unauthorized experiments.

13. Do not use equipment without instruction.

14. Report *all* spills and accidents to your instructor immediately.

15. Never leave heat sources unattended.

16. When using hot plates, note that there is no visible sign that they are hot (such as a red glow). Always assume that hot plates are hot.

17. Use an appropriate apparatus when handling hot glassware.

18. Keep chemicals away from direct heat or sunlight.

19. Keep containers of alcohol, acetone, and other flammable liquids away from flames.

20. Do not allow any liquid to come into contact with electrical cords. Handle electrical connectors with dry hands. Do not attempt to disconnect electrical equipment that crackles, snaps, or smokes.

21. Upon completion of laboratory exercises, place all materials in the disposal areas designated by your instructor.

22. Do not pick up broken glassware with your hands. Use a broom and dustpan and discard the glass in designated glass waste containers; never discard with paper waste.

23. Wear disposable gloves when working with blood, other body fluids, or mucous membranes. Change gloves after possible contamination and wash hands immediately after gloves are removed.

24. The disposal symbol indicates that items that may have come in contact with body fluids should be placed in your lab's designated container. It also refers to liquid wastes that should not be poured down the drain into the sewage system.

25. Leave the laboratory clean and organized for the next student.

26. Wash your hands with liquid or powdered soap prior to leaving the laboratory.

27. The biohazard symbol indicates procedures that may pose health concerns.

The caution symbol points out instruments, substances, and procedures that require special attention to safety. These symbols appear throughout this manual.

Measurement Conversions

Metric to American Standard	American Standard to Metric

Length

1 mm = 0.039 inches	1 inch = 2.54 cm
1 cm = 0.394 inches	1 foot = 0.305 m
1 m = 3.28 feet	1 yard = 0.914 m
1 m = 1.09 yards	1 mile = 1.61 km

Volume

1 mL = 0.0338 fluid ounces	1 fluid ounce = 29.6 mL
1 L = 4.23 cups	1 cup = 237 mL
1 L = 2.11 pints	1 pint = 0.474 L
1 L = 1.06 quarts	1 quart = 0.947 L
1 L = 0.264 gallons	1 gallon = 3.79 L

Mass

1 mg = 0.0000353 ounces	1 ounce = 28.3 g
1 g = 0.0353 ounces	1 pound = 0.454 kg
1 kg = 2.21 pounds	

Temperature

To convert temperature:

$$^\circ C = \frac{5}{9}(F - 32) \qquad\qquad ^\circ F = \frac{9}{5}C + 32$$

Contents

INTRODUCTION

The laboratory sessions are an important part of this course. They will provide you with the opportunity to experience science as a scientist. You will conduct experiments; collect and analyze data; and form conclusions based on your data. To be successful, you must come to lab prepared and carefully follow the directions contained in this manual and provided by your instructor. The lab manual, textbook and any other necessary materials suggested by the instructor should be brought to each lab session. The lab exercise should be read **before** coming to lab. The laboratory safety rules listed below must be followed.

MITCHELL COLLEGE
Lab Safety Rules

1.) **FOLLOW the SAFETY RULES stated by the INSTRUCTOR.**
2.) Wash hands and face QUICKLY with soap and water if a chemical is contacted.
3.) Never mouth-pipette a reagent, use the pipette bulbs provided.
4.) Use proper protection when working with hot glassware.
5.) Never perform an unauthorized experiment or work in the laboratory without proper supervision.
6.) ONLY your lab manual (or notebook) and the equipment necessary for an experiment should be on the lab bench.
7.) NEVER eat, drink or smoke in the laboratory.
8.) Know the location and use of all safety equipment in the laboratory.
9.) Discard of all waste as instructed for each experiment:
   - Never pour any waste down the drain without the permission of the instructor.
   - Only paper should be disposed of in the waste baskets.
   - Only use the designated container for broken glass.

10.) Report ALL accidents to the instructor. DON'T PANIC, ask for help.
11.) At the end of lab, return CLEAN equipment to its proper place, clear the lab bench of all equipment and wipe down the bench with a wet sponge.
12.) **ALWAYS wash your hands with soap and water before leaving the lab.**

<u>INTRODUCTION (Continued)</u>

To help you and your classmates successfully complete this course there are specific classroom behaviors that are required.

<u>Attendance</u>: Class attendance is expected and necessary for fully understanding the material covered in this course. After 3 absences, each absence (including tardiness by more than 10 minutes and early departure), will result in a decrease, by 2 points, of your participation grade in this course **(regardless of the reason). If more than 3 lab exercises are missed, the course will no longer fulfill the lab science requirement** and will count only as a 3 credit non-lab elective. There are no make-up classroom activities or labs.

<u>Academic Honesty</u>: Any individual assignments or papers which are plagiarized will receive a grade of zero. Please refer to the current Mitchell College student handbook or the catalog for more complete information regarding academic honesty.

<u>College Policy on Student Electronic Devices in the Classroom</u>: It is the right of every college student to be educated in an environment that is free from distraction from the educational activities being conducted in the classroom. To support students' right to a distraction-free educational environment, the following policy on use of electronic devices in the classroom is recommended to all faculty and students at Mitchell College:

- All electronic devices, including cell phones, MP3 players, iPods, or pagers, must be turned off during class time.
- In the case of medical emergency, or family need, when contact with the student is required, a cell phone may be left on during class time, with permission from the instructor. The cell phone must be set to vibrate to minimize the level of distraction for other students.
- Laptops are to be used only in the following circumstances:
    - As an approved reasonable accommodation for a student with a disability certified by the Office of Disability Support Services/Learning Resource Center. Laptops used for the purpose of disability accommodation are restricted to this purpose only and may not be used for other purposes.
    - There has been prior permission granted by the instructor to an individual student.
    - There is a classroom requirement for laptop use initiated by the instructor.
- A student's use of electronic devices in the classroom without prior permission, including cell phones, MP3 players, iPods, or pagers may result in the student being requested to leave the classroom, and an absence may be recorded for the student for that class.
- **After one warning, you will counted as absent for the class.**

<u>Other Disruptive Behaviors</u>: It is the right of every college student to be educated in an environment that is free from distraction from the educational activities being conducted in the classroom. To support students' right to a distraction-free educational environment, **students engaged in any other types of disruptive behavior will be asked to leave the classroom, and will be counted as absent for the class.**

Late Assignments: To achieve success in this course it is important that your assignments are turned in on time. Late assignments will lose 10 points and will **NOT** be accepted once graded and returned to students. Lab assignments will not be accepted if you have not participated in the lab exercise. Extra credit assignments, such as the lexicons, **will NOT receive any credit if they are late.** Please see the syllabus for more details concerning assignments.

MITCHELL COLLEGE

Student Agreement

I have studied, I understand, and I agree to follow the safety rules and classroom behaviors required for this course. I have located all emergency equipment and know how to use it. I understand that I may be dismissed from the classroom for failure to comply with stated safety and classroom behavior regulations.

Signature: _____

Print Name: _____

Date: _____

Course: _____

Instructor: _____

FUNDAMENTALS OF LIFE SCIENCE

ASSIGNMENT TRACKING SHEET

Assignment	Grade
QUIZZES	
✓ Q1	
✓ Q2	
✓ Q3	
✓ Q4	
✓ Q5	
✓ Q6	
✓ Q7	
ASSIGNMENTS	
✓ H1 - Gatorade	
✓ H2 -Macromolecule	
✓ H3 - Create a Protein	
✓ H4 - Mitosis/Meiosis Video	
✓ H5 - Genetics	
✓ H6 - Miracle of Life Video	
✓ H7- Nutritional Analysis	
LABS	
✓ L1 - Microscopy/Petri Dish	
✓ L2 - Diffusion	
✓ L3- Osmotic Pressure	
✓ L3 - Enzymes	
✓ L4 - Photosynthesis	
✓ L5 - Mitosis/Meiosis Lab	
✓ L6 – Animal Examination	
SERVICE LEARNING	
✓ SR1-Biodiversity Assignment	
✓ SR2-Project	
✓ SR3-Report	
✓ SRX-Extra Credit	
LEXICONS (EXTRA CREDIT)	**CHAPTERS COMPLETED:**

Absences:	Late Arrivals:
1._____	1._____
2._____	2._____
*3._____	*3._____
*4._____	*4._____
*5._____	*5._____

*POINTS DEDUCTED FROM PARTICIPATION GRADE

Class Activity: FLASHLIGHT/SCIENTIFIC METHOD

You will use the "Scientific Method" to determine what is wrong with your flashlight and answer the following questions:

1.) What are your observations?

2.) What is your question?

3.) What is your hypothesis?

4.) What is your prediction?

5.) What is the design of your controlled experiment? your independent variable? your dependent variable?

6.) What are the results of your experiment?

7.) What is your conclusion?

8.) Are there any variables that you did not consider in the original design of your experiment?

Assignment: The Gatorade Story-Scientific Method

Is Science in You? The Science Behind Gatorade:

Introduction:
In this lesson, you will review the scientific method by studying the development of Gatorade sports drinks. After viewing the presentation in class (you can review "The Gatorade Story" on your instructor's web page), answer these questions:

1. What observation was made by UF coaches and scientists?
2. What question did they formulate?
3. What data were already available?
4. What hypothesis did the scientists form?
5. How was that hypothesis tested?
6. What were the results of that testing?
7. What were the scientists' conclusions?

Please type your answers and include your name, date, and BI143 section on your paper.

Classroom Activity: EVOLUTION

Peppered Moth *(Biston betularia)* Simulation:

A light-colored, speckled variety of the Peppered Moth, *biston betularia,* was the predominant form found in Manchester, England prior to the Industrial Revolution. The coloring of this moth was a camouflage against the light-colored bark of trees in the forests of Manchester and protected the moths from predators. In 1848 a dark-colored variety of the Peppered Moth was reported. By the middle of the 19th century the burning of massive amounts of coal to support the factories of the Industrial Revolution began to produce soot that covered the trees in Manchester. By 1895 the dark variety of the Peppered Moth represented 98% of the population in Manchester. This is an example of **Industrial Melanism.** Industrial Melanism is the adaptation of a population to pollution.

Purpose:

In this activity you will simulate how color affects an organism's ability to survive in different environments.

Materials:

Sheet of white paper
Sheet of speckled paper
Forceps
Clock with Second Hand
30 speckled paper circles (made with hole punch)
30 white paper circles (made with hole punch)

Procedure: (The class will be divided into 6 groups)

Each group will:

1. **Place a sheet of white paper on the table and have one person spread 30 white circles and 30 speckled circles over the surface.**
2. **A second person will then use forceps to pick up as many of the circles as possible in 10 seconds.**
3. **Repeat steps one and two with 30 white circles and 30 speckled circles on a sheet of speckled paper.**
4. **Record your data and the other groups' data on the data sheet provided.**
5. **Analyze your data by answering the questions on the data sheet.**

Name of Group Members:

_____

_____

Peppered Moth Simulation Data Sheet

Group #1		Number of Circles Remaining	
Trial #	Background Paper	Speckled Circles	White Circles
1	white		
2	speckled		
Group #2		Number Remaining	
Trial #	Background	Speckled Circles	White Circles
1	white		
2	speckled		
Group #3		Number Remaining	
Trial #	Background	Speckled Circles	White Circles
1	white		
2	speckled		
Group #4		Number Remaining	
Trial #	Background	Speckled Circles	White Circles
1	white		
2	speckled		
Group #5		Number Remaining	
Trial #	Background	Speckled Circles	White Circles
1	white		
2	speckled		
Group #6		Number Remaining	
Trial #	Background	Speckled Circels	White Circles
1	white		
2	speckled		

<u>**Analysis:**</u>

1. How does this simulation compare to the change in the population of Peppered Moths in Manchester, England during the Industrial Revolution?

2. What would you predict the next generation of "moths" to look like after trial 1? What about the next generation of "moths" after trial 2?

3. How does the simulation model natural selection?

17

Class Activity: EVOLUTION II

Name: _____

Jelly Bean Activity and Assignment

1.) Each group will record the number and color of the jelly beans in their container.

Color:	Number:

2.) One person in the group will evenly distribute the jelly beans on the ground within the borders of a hula hoop.

3.) A second person in the group will be chosen as the predator.

4.) The predator will have EXACTLY one minute to pick up as many jelly beans as possible.

5.) A third member of the group will be the "timer" for this activity.

6.) At the end of one minute, the color and number of the "captured" jelly beans will be recorded.

Color:	Number:

7.) Create a bar graph comparing the number of jelly beans of each color in the original container to the number of jelly beans "captured" by the predator.

8.) Explain how your results relate to the concept of Natural Selection.

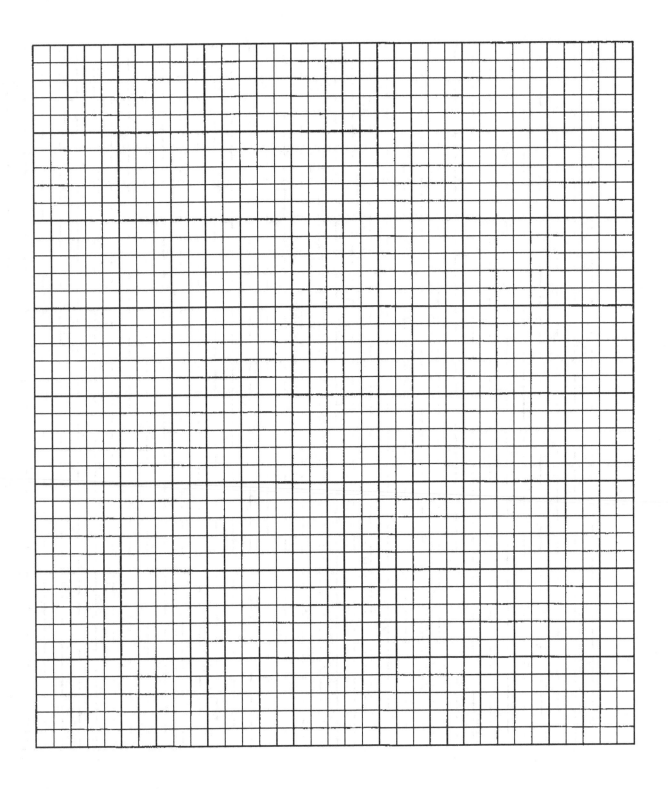

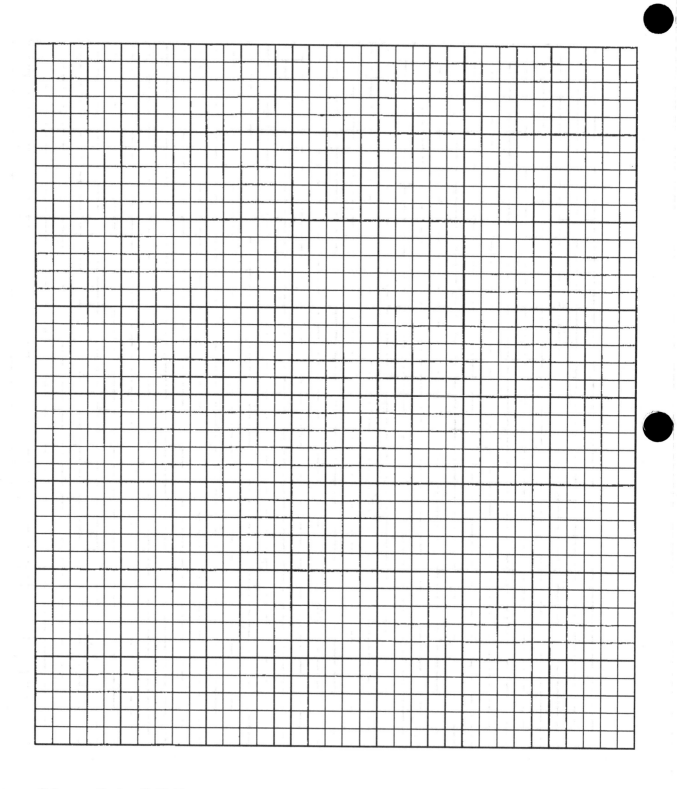

Class Activity: A Dichotomous Key to Hardware

You and your lab team are scientists, hired by the Kingdom of Hardware. Your job is to develop a classification system for all the items in this kingdom. The system you develop must include SCIENTIFIC NAMES of each of the groups and members of each group. Your final product must include a classification key so the residents of the Kingdom of Hardware will be able to classify the items after you have left.

Your plastic cup contains one of each item. Develop a dichotomous key that can be used to classify the items of the Kingdom of Hardware. Be sure to TEST your key to make sure it works for all items. Each group must submit a copy of the key developed.

Suggested procedure:

1) Sort your items into related groups.
2) Give the individuals tentative scientific names. Try to make the names descriptive and Latin sounding. Our species, for example, is *Homo sapiens* (thinking man).
3) Construct a key so that any student could identify your items.
4) Test your team's key by having another team try it while you try their key.

SERVICE LEARNING PROJECT:

Individual Biodiversity Assignment: Introduction to the Mitchell Beach Restoration

Name: _____ Due: _____

Do you know an oak from a maple? Oriental Bittersweet from Japanese Knotweed? Poison ivy from...?????? **Sketch and learn to identify the species of plants listed below. Draw their leaf shape and arrangement, but also draw or describe any other identifying characteristics (fruit, bark, etc.), as noted below. Also note any other interesting facts that you learn, such as medicinal uses, and whether it is a native plant, invasive, or poisonous.**

Make sure to take a look at the different reference books available on plant identification, ecology and uses. If you become interested in one of the plants, you might want to look it up, and see what else you can learn about it.

Trees at Mitchell Beach

Maples: There are many species of maples. Which one do we have on this beach? Can you guess if it is invasive or native? ***Draw the leaves in the spaces provided. Label with species name and common name.***

The trees below both have compound leaves. How can you tell them apart?

Black locust: A somewhat invasive tree, native to the more southern US, but survives as a street tree, and has gotten into native forests. A member of the bean family, check out its fruit! It also has very fragrant, white flowers in the springtime. ***Draw the leaves in the spaces provided. Label with species name and common name.***

Tree of Heaven (*Ailanthus*): A very invasive tree, found growing on the sides of buildings, in cracks of pavement, wherever a bit of soil can be found. <u>A Tree Grows in Brooklyn</u> was written about this tree. Has a characteristic gland at the base of every leaf blade. Feel for it. Produces lots of fruits in big bunches, which are very visible in autumn. ***Draw the leaves in the spaces provided. Label with species name and common name.***

Some Important Native and Invasive Herbs at Mitchell Beach

Poison ivy: You need to know this plant! There is a lot of it on the Mitchell Beach dune. It is a native, but an unpleasant one in some ways. It exudes an oil that contains a compound called urushiol. This compound, when it gets on the skin, produces a very unpleasant itchy rash, that lasts about two weeks (seems like forever). **"Leaves in three, let it be!"** The leaves are arranged in whorls of three. The leaves are shiny, red in spring and fall, green in summer. It is a vine, which means it twines its way up walls and fences, and the trunks of other plants, using them for support. So you can think you are leaning against a friendly oak tree, and get poison ivy all over you. Prevention? Recognize it and don't touch it. The cure? Wash with detergent and cold water when you get home and launder your clothes, to remove the oil if you think you have touched it.

Oriental Bittersweet: Sometimes grows as a vine, sometimes as a bush. Very common, with yellow leaves that change color very early in the fall, green in summer. It possesses beautiful red and yellow fruit. ***Find a specimen of this herbaceous plant and sketch it in the spaces provided. Label with species name and common name.***

Mugwort: An invasive plant, that can cover empty lots, and covers much of Mitchell Beach. It and its relative, ragweed, produce a lot of pollen, which causes allergies during the summer months. It does contain a compound called artemisin (check out its scientific name) which is very helpful in treating malaria. ***Find a specimen of this herbaceous plant and sketch it in the spaces provided. Label with species name and common name.***

Japanese Knotweed: An invasive plant, very common in our area. Japanese knotweed spreads quickly to form dense thickets that exclude native vegetation and greatly alter natural ecosystems. It poses a significant threat to riverine areas, where it can survive severe floods and is able to rapidly colonize scoured shores and islands. Once established, populations are extremely persistent. ***Find a specimen of this herbaceous plant and sketch it in the spaces provided. Label with species name and common name.***

Goldenrods: A very pretty group of native plants that bloom in late summer and fall. They are given a bad rap as causing allergies from their pollen, as ragweed and mugwort do. Not so. Their pollen is distributed by bees, not by the wind, so it is heavier and rarely found in the air currents where it may disturb sensitive sinuses. Found on the foredune at Mitchell Beach. ***Find a specimen of this herbaceous plant and sketch it in the spaces provided. Label with species name and common name.***

Identify, draw and make notes about any other species you find at Mitchell Beach. Is the plant invasive? Native?

PLANT SKETCHES and INFORMATION:

PLANT SKETCHES and INFORMATION:

PLANT SKETCHES and INFORMATION:

PLANT SKETCHES and INFORMATION:

SERVICE LEARNING PROJECT:

Individual Biodiversity Assignment II: DUE:_____

The Biodiversity Activity simulating the spread of disease in a Douglas Fir monoculture versus an old growth forest was to help you begin to understand the importance of biodiversity to the "health" of the environment and the purpose of the Mitchell Beach Restoration project. Please **TYPE** the answers to the questions below. **THIS IS AN INDIVIDUAL ASSIGNMENT.**

1. What does biological diversity mean?
2. How does biodiversity benefit humans?
3. In which forest would you need to use more chemicals to control disease: the Douglas fir forest or the more diversified, old growth forest? Why?
4. Which forest would have more diversity of wildlife? Why?
5. Growing one plant, as is the case of growing only Douglas fir, is called monoculture. Give an example of growing one plant on farms. Why would you need to use more insecticides in this monoculture? Is this good or bad?
6. If you wanted to help wildlife, what would you do with regards to the landscaping of your own home?
7. What are the major causes of the decrease in biodiversity?
8. How do invasive plants decrease biodiversity?
9. How would global warming global warming affect biodiversity?
10. How does this simulation relate to the Mitchell Beach Restoration project?

Class Activity: Types of Compounds Activity

Name: _____

The instructor will perform the following demonstrations and students will be asked to predict the results:

1.) A scoop of $CuCl_2$ crystals are dissolved a 150mL beaker of distilled water. What type of substance might $CuCl_2$ be?

_____

2.) The $CuCl_2$ aqueous solution is tested with the light bulb apparatus. What type of substance is $CuCl_2$?

_____

3.) Five test tubes will be set up with the following contents:
   a. Two with a scoop of $CuCl_2$ crystals
   b. Two with a scoop of iodine crystals
   c. One with a dropper full of hexane

4.) A dropper full of water is added to the hexane. What type of substance is hexane?

_____

5.) A dropper full of water is added to one test tube of $CuCl_2$ and one test tube of iodine. What type of substance is iodine?

_____

6.) A dropper full of hexane is added to one test tube of $CuCl_2$ and one test tube of iodine. What will happen? Why?

_____

_____

_____

7.) The test tube with the aqueous solution of $CuCl_2$ is mixed with the hexane solution of iodine. Draw what the test tube mixture will look like and to explain your prediction.

8.) Critical Thinking Question: Why is it more difficult to clean up PCB water contamination than oil spills? Both PCBs and oil are nonpolar molecular compounds, but PCBs are denser than water and oil is less dense than water.

Assignment: Biological Molecules Chart

Name: _____   Due: _____

Living cells are made up primarily of four types of large molecular compounds: carbohydrates, lipids, proteins and nucleic acids. Most of these molecules are themselves composed of many units of smaller molecules. In preparation for our class discussion, complete the chart below for each biological molecule; identifying its smaller molecular units, its polarity (polar or nonpolar), its reaction with water (hydrophilic or hydrophobic), and a major cellular function.

Biological Molecule	Smaller Molecular Unit(s)	Polarity (Polar or Nonpolar)	Reaction with Water (Hydrophilic or Hydrophobic)	Major Cellular Function
Carbohydrate				
Lipid (Specifically Fats or Triglycerides)				
Proteins				
Nucleic Acids				

LAB: INTRODUCTION TO THE MICROSCOPE

Much of the biological world is large and visible with the unaided eye. Tiny organisms and the cells that make up humans and other larger living things are very small, however and must be viewed with the assistance of a microscope. Although you may have previously used a microscope, it will be necessary to familiarize yourself with the instruments used in this laboratory and to review the parts and how they operate. Please learn the name and function of each of the parts of the compound light microscope listed below. The particular microscope you're using may or may not have every feature described.

An ARM, a BASE and a BODY TUBE
An OCULAR (usually 10x, but be sure to check the one on the scope you're using)
A REVOLVING NOSEPIECE, to which the objectives are attached
Two to four OBJECTIVES (usually 4X, 10X, 40 or 43X, 97X)
Two focusing knobs – COARSE and FINE adjustment
The STAGE, with either STAGE CLIPS or a MECHANICAL STAGE CONTROL
A SUBSTAGE CONDENSER (some model s)
An IRIS DIAPHRAGM, or DISC DIAPHRAGM or other light control
A built-in ILLUMINATOR or a MIRROR to direct light

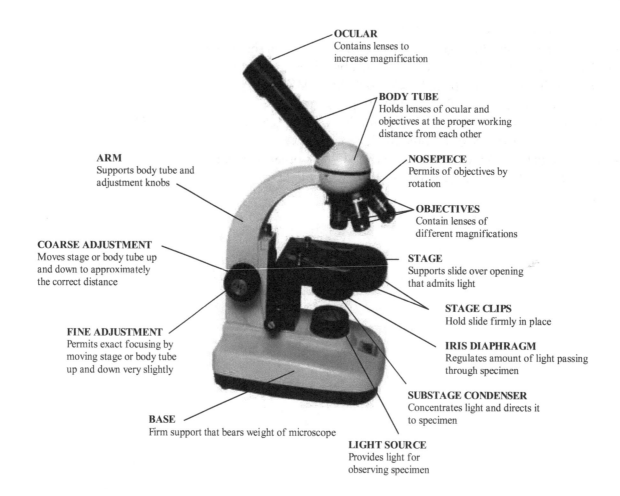

OCULAR
Contains lenses to
increase magnification

BODY TUBE
Holds lenses of ocular and
objectives at the proper working
distance from each other

NOSEPIECE
Permits of objectives by
rotation

ARM
Supports body tube and
adjustment knobs

OBJECTIVES
Contain lenses of
different magnifications

COARSE ADJUSTMENT
Moves stage or body tube up
and down to approximately
the correct distance

STAGE
Supports slide over opening
that admits light

STAGE CLIPS
Hold slide firmly in place

FINE ADJUSTMENT
Permits exact focusing by
moving stage or body tube
up and down very slightly

IRIS DIAPHRAGM
Regulates amount of light passing
through specimen

SUBSTAGE CONDENSER
Concentrates light and directs it
to specimen

BASE
Firm support that bears weight of microscope

LIGHT SOURCE
Provides light for
observing specimen

INTRODUCTION TO OBSERVING CELLS WITH THE COMPOUND LIGHT MICROSCOPE

● 1) Clear a space on the lab bench for your microscope and obtain a microscope, carrying it with TWO HANDS, as demonstrated by your instructor.

2) Set the base of the microscope squarely in front of you on the table. If your microscope uses external illumination, arrange the lamp so that its bulb is about 6 inches in front of the mirror.

3) Look at the numbers on the ocular. What magnification is possible with this ocular?   1) _____

4) Be sure that the lowest power objective – the shortest one – is in "click-stop" position.
   What magnification is this low power objective? 2) _____

5) Find the coarse focusing knob and determine if focusing is done by moving the microscope **body** or the **stage**. Never decrease this distance while trying to establish good focus.   Why? 3) _____

6) IF YOUR MICROSCOPE HAS A SUBSTAGE CONDENSER and iris diaphragm, find their controls. Move the condenser up, if necessary, so that its lens is flush with the under surface of the stage. Find the handle of the iris diaphragm for controlling light intensity.

7) IF YOUR MICROSCOPE HAS A DISC DIAPHRAGM, instead of an iris diaphragm, revolve it to see that its several apertures control light intensity. Some microscopes have these color-coded with the objectives. Make sure you can feel and hear the disc diaphragm lock into position.

● 8) Looking into the ocular, be sure that you have a "full-moon" field of view. If you don't, make sure that the objective is clicked into place. If your microscope has external illumination and a mirror, you'll have to focus the mirror.

9) Reduce the light level so that the field of view is not too bright.

10) Prepare a wet-mount of living organisms, following the directions given below:

MAKING A TEMPORARY WET-MOUNT TO OBSERVE LIVING ORGANISMS

   a) Use the dropping pipette in the specimen container to place a small drop of the specimen culture onto a clean glass slide.
   b) Put one edge of a coverslip beside the specimen and lower the opposite edge so as not to trap tiny air bubbles. If you've used the right amount of fluid material, it should spread out to all edges of the coverslip without floating it. If you have far too much liquid, you can absorb the excess with a Kimwipe™.
   c) Use the lowest power objective to start your observation. The specimens may be protozoa (microscopic animals) or algae (tiny aquatic plants). Your instructor can tell you more about them and may provide pictures so you can identify what you observe.
   d) If the sample includes fast-swimming creatures, you may want to slow them down for better observation. To do so, just make another preparation, this time adding equal amounts of specimen and methyl cellulose or Proto-Slo™. You may need to reduce the amount of light entering the stage as you look for live organisms on your slide. Enjoy observing your specimens for a while.

e) Make some sketches of your specimens on the last page of this report.
f) Look at some of your classmates' specimens, and feel free to make another slide if your first effort is disappointing. You may wish to refer to some manuals to identify what's swimming around on the microscope slides.

11) Now prepare to examine some of your very own cells.
a) Discard your coverslip in the wastebasket, rinse off your slide and wash your hands.
b) Place a drop of distilled water on your clean microscope slide and set the slide on your lab table.
c) Use the broad end of a clean, flat toothpick to <u>gently</u> scrape the inside of your cheek. Remember, we're looking for epidermal cells, not blood cells.
d) Stir the scraping into the water on your slide and add a coverslip.
e) To stain your slide, follow these directions:
    i) First add a drop of stain just at the edge of one side of the coverslip.
    ii) Pull the stain under the coverslip by touching a piece of tissue paper (such as one of the squares that separated the coverslips) or a Kimwipe™ to the OPPOSITE side of the coverslip. See the sketch below:

12) Find your cells using the low-power objective of your microscope; find the nucleus, a centrally located spherical body within the cytoplasm of each cell.

13) On the page with the circles, make a **sketch** of an individual cell at low power. Make certain that the cell you're observing is completely centered and focused before you switch to medium power.

14) Switch to medium power (100X). Since most microscopes are **parfocal**, as long as your image is centered at one magnification, it will still be in the center, and roughly in focus, when you switch to the next power. How do you think the cell will appear when you see it at medium power (100X)?

      4) Will it **_look_** a) smaller   _____?
                  b) larger   _____?
         or c) the same size_____?
      5) What do you think will happen to the **ACTUAL SIZE** of the cell when you see it at medium power (100X)?
      6) Will it **_be_** a) smaller   _____?
           b) larger   _____?
        or c) the same size _____?

15) Make sure that the objective clicks into place. Using fine adjustment, refine the focus at medium power and **draw** the same cell in proportion in the 100X circle.
Does the cell occupy the same amount of the circle (the microscope field) as it was at 40X? 7) _____

                                 Are you surprised?   8) _____
                                 What has changed?   9) _____

16) **BE CAREFUL WITH THIS NEXT STEP !!**
   Making sure that the cell is in the center of the field at medium power (100X), carefully click the high power objective in place. Refine the focus and observe the cell again.
        Now how big much of the circle does the cell occupy? 10) _____
                         Are you surprised?   11) _____
              Should the actual size change?   12) _____
                What is it that changes?   13) _____
Make a new sketch on the sketches page.

Sketch of **Human Cheek Cell**, observed at **40X**   Sketch of **Human Cheek Cell**, observed at **10 0X**

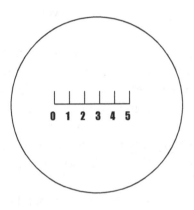

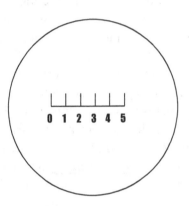

Sketch of **Human Cheek Cell**, observed at **400X**   Sketch of *Elodea* **cells**, observed at **400X**

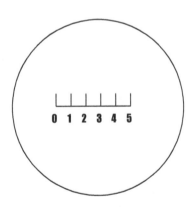

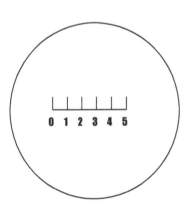

Observe plant cells with the light microscope

Young leaves at the growing tip of *Elodea*, a typical aquarium plant, are particularly well-suited for studying cell structure because these leaves are only a few layers thick.

1) With forceps, remove a single leaf, mount it on a slide in a drop of distilled water and cover with a coverslip. Examine the leaf first under the low-power objective. Then concentrate your study on several cells using the high power objective. What shape are these cells? 14) _____ What do you think these green circles within each cell are ? 15) _____
(Hint: What makes plants green?) These organelles, which function in photosynthesis, are typical of green plants. You may see numerous dark lines running parallel to the long axis of the leaf. These are the **intercellular spaces** that contain air. Plant cells, just like animal cells, are surrounded by a **cell membrane** enclosing their cytoplasm. The **cell wall**, one structure distinguishing plant cells from animal cells, may be visible as a clear area surrounding the cell membrane around the cytoplasm.

In the middle portion of each *Elodea* cell is a large, clear, **central vacuole**, which occupies most of the cell's interior. The **chloroplasts** occur in the cytoplasm surrounding the vacuole, so they will appear to be in different locations, depending on where you focus in the cell.

Locate the **nucleus** within the cytoplasm. It will appear as a clear or slightly amber body that is slightly larger than the chloroplasts. You may nee d to examine several cells to find a clearly defined nucleus.

What structures have you observed in these plant cells that are absent in animal cell s?
16) _____
Record this sketch on the sketches page (the page with the circles).

EXAMINATION OF PROKARYOTIC ORGANISMS

Step 1: In preparation for the next lab exercise, you will be given a Petri plate filled with nutrient agar on which you will grow bacteria. With a sterile swab, sample some area in the classroom or surrounding areas of the building. Gently swipe the swab over the surface of the plate – don't gouge out the agar – and discard your swab as instructed. Using the available marker, label the bottom of the plate with your initials, building area swabbed and date. The p lates will be incubated at 37° until the next class period, when you will examine them according to the protocol described below.

Step 2: Examine the colonies of live bacteria on the Petri plates you exposed previously and describe the following colony f eatures:

Shape (round, irregular, etc.) _____ _____

Size (use a metric ruler)_____

Texture (smooth, rough, moist, dry, fuzzy)_____

Elevation (flat, raised, etc.) _____

Color (white, cream, yellow, red, green) _____

Sketch some sample colonies in the circles below:

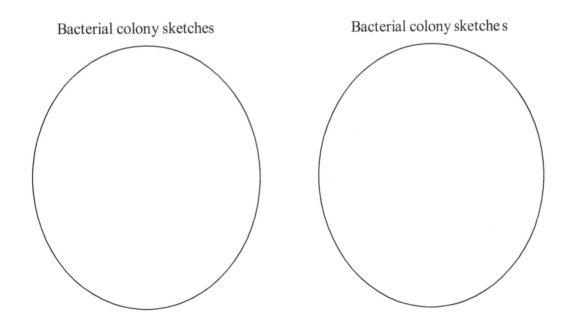

Bacterial colony sketches

Bacterial colony sketche s

LAB: DIFFUSION and OSMOSIS

Laboratory Objectives

After completing this lab, you should be able to:
1. Describe the mechanism of diffusion on the molecular level.
2. Explain the effects of temperature and concentration on diffusion.
3. Distinguish between osmosis and diffusion.
4. Define the term differentially permeable membrane.
5. Describe the effects of hypotonic, isotonic and hypertonic solutions on plant and animal tissues.

Introduction

To stay alive, living cells regulate the exchange of substances with their external environment. Virtually all substances leaving or entering a cell are dissolved in water, the major component of all cells. The cytoplasm and extracellular environment of cells are aqueous (water) **solutions** in which many organic and inorganic **solutes**, such as salt and sugar, are dissolved. Water is the **solvent** of these solutions.

The movement of substances, into and out of all cells, is controlled by the plasma membrane. The plasma membrane is composed of a phospholipids bilayer containing embedded and surface protein molecules. These membranes are **differentially permeable**, allowing water and other small molecules to pass freely while regulating the movement of other substances. The organelles of eukaryotic cells are also surrounded by differentially permeable membranes.

Plasma membranes regulate the movement of dissolved substances by a number of different methods. The most common method of moving dissolved solutes across a plasma membrane is **diffusion.** Diffusion is the movement of molecules from an area of higher concentration to an area of lower concentration. This type of movement requires no expenditure of cellular energy (ATP). Molecules are always in motion; it is this **kinetic energy** that drives diffusion. As long as nothing prevents the free movement of molecules, they will diffuse until **equilibrium** is reached. Equilibrium is the state when the concentration of solute molecules becomes equally distributed. At equilibrium the solute molecules continue to move but there is no net change in the concentration.

Water, the solvent for living cells, can freely move across plasma membranes. The diffusion of water molecules across a differentially permeable membrane (such as the plasma membrane) is called **Osmosis**. Water molecules will move from an area of higher water concentration to an area of lower water concentration. The terms, **hypotonic**, **isotonic** and **hypertonic** are frequently used to explain the movement of water molecules between solutions of varying concentrations. A hypotonic solution has a lower solute concentration compared to another solution. A hypertonic solution has a higher solute concentration compared to another solution. Solutions with equal solute concentrations are isotonic to each other. **Water molecules will always move from a hypotonic solution into a hypertonic solution.**

During this lab you will investigate the processes of diffusion and osmosis in living cells and in models of cells created with **dialysis tubing**. Dialysis tubing is a differentially permeable membrane. It contains pores (4.8 microns in diameter) that allow the free passage of small molecules (such as water), but obstruct the passage of large molecules (such as sucrose).

I. Effect of Temperature on Rate of Diffusion of Solutes - Demonstration

The rate of diffusion is affected by factors such as temperature, solute concentration and the size of solute molecules.

Procedure:
Your lab instructor will put several drops of methylene blue dye into each of two cylinders, one containing cold water and another containing hot water.

How does temperature affect the rate of diffusion?

_____

Which solvent has the greater kinetic energy?

_____

II. Effect of Molecular Concentration on Rate of Osmosis

This experiment uses dialysis tubing as a model for the differentially permeable plasma membrane. The dialysis tubing will be filled with different concentrations of sucrose solutions, representing the "cytoplasm" of the cell. Each dialysis tube will be placed in a finger bowl containing water or a sucrose solution. This will represent the "extracellular fluid" surrounding living cells. The water molecules can freely pass through the pores in the dialysis tubing, but the sucrose molecules are too large to fit through the pores.

Note: Each lab group will be responsible for one cell. Data will be shared at the end of the experiment.

Procedure:
1. Soak a strip of dialysis tubing in a beaker of tap water for at least one minute. Do not let the dialysis tubing dry out. (Place a sixth strip of dialysis tubing in the beaker to be used later in exercise III).

2. Set up 5 finger bowls (numbered 1 to 5) and using a graduated cylinder, fill each with 100 mL of the "extracellular fluid" indicated in the Table I below. Each group will be assigned one of the five finger bowls.

3. For each dialysis tube, twist one end of the tube, fold in over twice, and tie it tightly with a piece of string. Clip the excess string with scissors.

4. Using a small graduated cylinder, measure 15 mL of the "cytoplasm" solution indicated in Table I below. Using a small funnel, fill each dialysis tube with the correct "cytoplasm" solution.

5. Squeeze out the air in each tube and tie off the open end as indicated in step 3.

6. Weigh each tube immediately to the nearest tenth of a gram and place each one in the finger bowl containing the correct "extracellular fluid". Record these weights in table I at time zero.

7. Weigh each tube every 10 minutes for a total of 40 minutes and record the weights in Table I below. Make sure that you wipe off any excess solution with a paper towel before weighing the tubes.

8. Complete the table below using data collected by the other groups.

9. Plot the **weight changes** for each tube on the graph paper provided at the end of this section. Label each line with the corresponding cell number (as indicated in the Table I below).

TABLE I

Cell #	Cytoplasm 15 mL	Extracellular Fluid 100 mL	0 Minutes	10 Minutes	20 Minutes	30 Minutes	40 Minutes
1	Water	Water	g	g	g	g	g
2	20% Sucrose	Water	g	g	g	g	g
3	40% Sucrose	Water	g	g	g	g	g
4	60% Sucrose	Water	g	g	g	g	g
5	Water	60% Sucrose	g	g	g	g	g

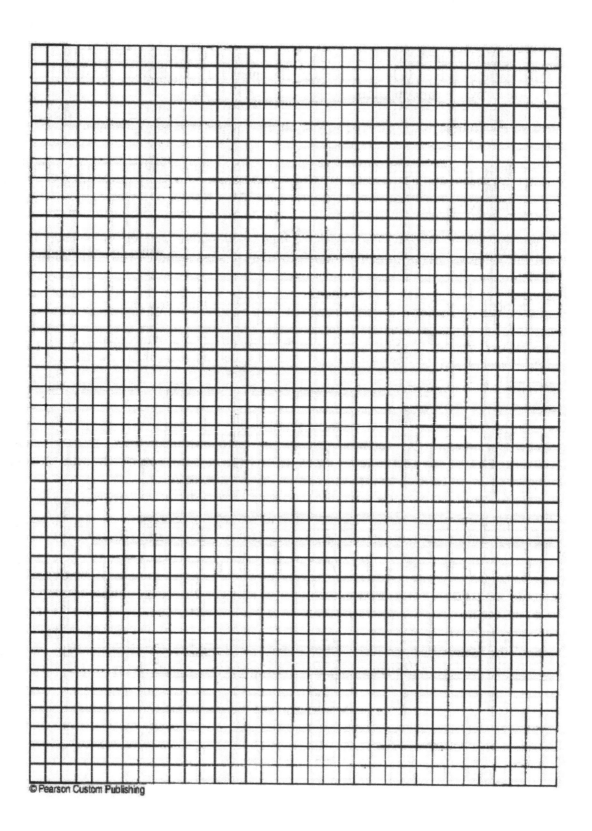

III. Permeability of Cell Membranes - Demonstration

Differentially permeable membranes permit the free passage of some substances and regulate the passage of others. In exercise II, you were able to study osmosis because only the water molecules could move through the pores of the dialysis tubing; the sucrose molecules were too large to fit through the pores. In this exercise you will use dialysis tubing as a model of a cell membrane and investigate its permeability to two different substances, iodine potassium iodide and starch. **Important Fact: When iodine potassium iodide is added to a starch solution, the solution turns a purple or black color.**

Procedure:
1. Tie off a water soaked strip of dialysis tubing as you did in exercise II.

2. Using a small graduated cylinder, measure 15 mL of a 0.1% starch solution and, using a small funnel, fill the tube with this solution.

3. Tie off the open end of the dialysis tube as you did in exercise II.

4. Using a graduated cylinder, measure 100 mL of water and pour it into a finger bowl.

5. Add several drops of iodine potassium iodide solution to the finger bowl. Record the color of the solution in Table II below.

6. Record the color of the starch solution in the dialysis tube and then place it into the finger bowl.

7. After 30 minutes, record the color of the solutions in the dialysis tube and the finger bowl in Table II below.

TABLE II

Solution Container	Original Color	Final Color
Dialysis Tube "Cell"		
Finger Bowl		

IV. Comparison of Plant Tissues Having Normal Turgor Pressure to Those with Plamolyzed Cells - Demonstration

In the previous exercise you observed plasmolysis on the cellular level. In this exercise you will observe the gross effects of plasmolysis on whole plant tissue.

Procedure:
Pick up one vegetable soaked in plain water and another soaked in a 20% salt (NaCl) solution. Compare by feeling the vegetables.

Which vegetable sample is crisp (demonstrates turgor pressure)?
_____

Which vegetable sample is wilted (demonstrates plasmolysis)?
_____

V. Post-Lab Questions

1. How does osmosis differ from diffusion?

2. If a 20% sucrose solution is separated from a 40% sucrose solution by a differentially permeable membrane, in which direction will the water move?

3. Animal cells, such as red blood cells, do not possess a rigid cell wall. The only boundary of the cell, the plasma membrane, is relatively fragile. What would you expect would happen to human red blood cells placed in a hypotonic solution?

4. You are about to make a salad and you discover that the lettuce is wilted. How might you restore its crispness?

5. Based on your knowledge of osmosis, why is it important to drink adequate amounts of water everyday?

6. Why can't a human being survive by drinking salt water? (Hint: Think about the movement of water molecules on the cellular level)

7. After a snowy winter when large quantities of salt have been used to keep highways safe, many of the evergreen trees along the sides of the road look "burned". Explain this observation.

8. Suppose that you wanted to dissolve a solute in water. Without shaking or stirring the solution, what might you do to increase the rate at which the solute would go into solution?

CLASS ACTIVITY: OSMOTIC PRESSURE

Background: Osmotic pressure can be defined as pressure that is exerted on cells (e.g. bacteria, fungi, protests) by their surrounding environment. The pressure exerted will affect the growth or another physical trait, such as pigment production, of the organism in some way. To this end, high levels of salt or sugar can be added to food as a preservative.

Purpose: To observe and record the effects of increasing concentrations of salt (sodium chloride) and sugar (sucrose) on the growth of several common food spoilage microorganisms.

Materials:

1. **Typical Cultures that can be used (may vary from instructor to instructor):**

   Escherichia coli

   Staphylococcus aureus

   Bacillus cereus

   Saccharomyces cerevisiae

2. **Sterile Applicator Sticks**

3. **Beaker of Disinfectant or Autoclave Bag**

4. **Media: Nutrient agar (control medium)**

   Nutrient agar + 0.5% sucrose

   Nutrient agar + 25% sucrose

   Nutrient agar + 50% sucrose

   Nutrient agar + 0.5% sodium chloride

   Nutrient agar + 15% sodium chloride

   Nutrient agar + 25% sodium chloride

Procedure: Each lab section will be split into four (4) groups. Each group will receive a plate of cells of one of the test microorganisms, four packages of applicator sticks and one of each type of nutrient agar plates.

1. **Remove an applicator stick from the package, being careful not to touch the cotton tip to any surface.**

2. **With the cotton end of the applicator stick pick up some of the cells from the plate provided. Then gently streak the surface of the agar in the center of the plate in a straight line as shown in figure 1 below (do not break the surface of the agar.**

Figure 1

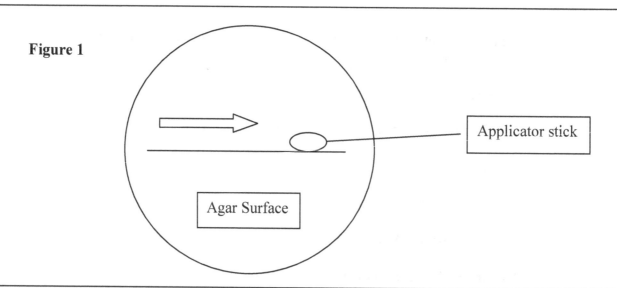

3. **Repeat steps 1 and 2 for each of the remaining agar plates in the series making sure to use a fresh applicator stick for each plate.**

4. **Label each plate with the name of the culture used and the name of the group. Place the plates in the 23°C incubator and allow them to grow for 3 days.**

5. **On the third day, the growth of the cultures are examined and compared.**

6. **The growth on the nutrient agar control plate will be scored as +++. The growth of the culture on the remaining plates will be compared to the control and scored as +++ (good growth), ++ (moderate growth), + (slight growth) or --- (no growth).**

7. **Record results in the following table for the whole class:**

Data Table:

Test Organism	Nutrient agar	0.5% sucrose agar	25% sucrose agar	50% sucrose agar
E. coli				
S. aureus				
S. cerevisiae				
B. cereus				

Test Organism	Nutrient agar	0.5% NaCl agar	15% NaCl agar	25% NaCl agar
E. coli				
S. aureus				
S. cerevisiae				
B. cereus				

Discussion: The majority of known microorganisms tend to grow best in an environment that exhibits a slightly lower osmotic pressure (hypotonic) than that found inside the cell. Most microorganisms can adapt to small changes in osmotic pressure created by their surrounding environment. While a few can tolerate significant changes in their osmotic environment, the vast majority are usually inhibited from growing or killed by osmotic pressure (hypertonic) created from high levels of sugars or salt. These high concentrations of sugars or salt work by making water unavailable to a cell and causing a condition known as plasmolysis in which water is lost from a cell. This negative effect on microorganisms has been a mainstay in human history for the preservation of foods along with freezing, smoking and dehydration of foods.

Microorganisms are ubiquitous and uncooked foods can play host to a large number of microbes. Growth of microbes on foodstuffs not only leads to spoilage of the food item in question but some microbes can produce toxins that can cause food poisoning. One in four Americans will experience the effects of food poisoning at least once in their lifetime.

The four microbes that are utilized in this exercise are potential food spoilers:

Students will set up the experiments in the **tall** test tubes at the work area and, after incubating the tubes, will transfer a portion of each experimental solution to a corresponding **short** test tube. Label the tubes before beginning the experiment so you don't get mixed up! Into the short tube you will also place 10 drops of water and finally you will add the Clinitest™ tablet to determine the range of enzyme activity. Before you actually perform the experiment, **predict** the results expected in the **Hypothesis** section of the lab report at the end of this exercise. When you have completed the experiment, **record** your team's results in the **Results** section and then, together with your team, develop a **one sentence** conclusion explaining these results and place that conclusion in the **Conclusion** section of your experiment.

I. Effect of Enzyme Concentration on Enzyme Activity

This group will examine how the amount or concentration of enzyme affects the rate of enzyme activity in a reaction.

1) Predict what you expect to happen and record this in the Hypothesis section at the end.
2) Label both the short and the tall test tubes with numbers 1 through 6, as indicated on the chart below:

Tube #	ml enzyme	ml H_2O	ml pH 4.4 buffer	ml sucrose	Enzyme concentration	Enzyme activity
1	5.00	5.00	2.00	None		
2	5.00	None	2.00	5.00		
3	2.50	2.50	2.00	5.00		
4	1.00	4.00	2.00	5.00		
5	0.50	4.50	2.00	5.00		
6	0.25	4.75	2.00	5.00		

3) Mix enzyme, H_2O, buffer and sucrose in the amounts indicated for each tube, according to the chart above.
4) Let the tubes sit in the test tube rack to incubate for 10 minutes.
5) Toward the end of the incubation time, add 10 drops of distilled water to the 5 short test tubes.
6) Once the incubation time ends, add 5 drops from tall tube #1 to short tube #1 and mix. Be sure to use a separate dropper for each of the 6 reaction tubes.
7) Repeat Step 6 for all the corresponding tall and short tubes, that is, 5 drops from tall tube #2 to short tube #2 and so on until all short tubes have reaction mixture added to the distilled water.
8) Add a Clinitest™ tablet to each short tube and swirl gently to mix. **BE CAREFUL**, as the contents of the tube will get hot, heating the tube itself.
9) Record the amount of activity (Results) in the table above **and** at the end of the report.
10) Consult with your teammates to form a conclusion that you will record at the end of the report.

2

II. Effect of pH on Enzyme Activity

This group will examine how the pH of the environment affects the rate of enzyme activity in a reaction. Each enzyme operates best at an **optimal** pH.

1) Predict what you expect to happen and record this in the Hypothesis section at the end.
2) Label both the short and the tall test tubes with numbers 1 through 4, as indicated on the chart below.
3) Set up the 4 tall test tubes according to the chart below, mixing enzyme, buffer and sucrose as indicated for each tube.

Tube #	ml enzyme	ml buffer	ml sucrose	Enzyme activity
1	5.00	2.00 pH 1.0	5.00	
2	5.00	2.00 pH 4.4	5.00	
3	5.00	2.00 pH 8.0	5.00	
4	5.00	2.00 pH 12.0	5.00	

4) Let the tubes sit in the test tube rack to incubate for 10 minutes.
5) Toward the end of the incubation time, add 10 drops of distilled water to the 5 short test tubes.
6) Once the incubation time ends, add 5 drops from tall tube #1 to short tube #1 and mix. Be sure to use a separate dropper for each of the 4 reaction tubes.
7) Repeat Step 6 for all the corresponding tall and short tubes, that is, 5 drops from tall tube #2 to short tube #2 and so on until all short tubes have reaction mixture added to the distilled water.
8) Add a Clinitest™ tablet to each short tube and swirl gently to mix. **BE CAREFUL**, as the contents of the tube will get hot, heating the tube itself.
9) Record the amount of activity (Results) in the table above and at the end of the report.
10) Consult with your teammates to form a conclusion that you will record at the end of the report.

3

III. Effect of Temperature on Enzyme Activity

This group will examine how the temperature of the environment affects the rate of enzyme activity in a reaction. Each enzyme operates best at an **optimal** temperature.

Tube #	ml enzyme	ml ph 4.4 buffer	ml sucrose	Temperature (degrees C)	Enzyme activity
1A	5.00	2.00	none	0°	
2A	5.00	2.00	none	___° (room temperature)	
3A	5.00	2.00	none	37°	
4A	5.00	2.00	none	100°	
1B	none	none	5.00	0°	
2B	none	none	5.00	___° (room temperature)	
3B	none	none	5.00	37°	
4B	none	none	5.00	100°	

1) Predict what you expect to happen and record this in the Hypothesis section at the end.
2) Label the 8 tall test tubes with numbers 1A through 4A and 1B through 4B, as indicated on the chart above.
3) Label the 4 short test tubes with the numbers 1 through 4.
4) Mix enzyme and buffer into tubes 1A, 2A, 3A, and 4A, as indicated on the chart above, and return these tubes to the test tube rack.
5) Add sucrose to tubes 1B, 2B, 3B and 4B and return these tubes to the test tube rack.
6) Place the tubes at their appropriate temperature to incubate for 5 minutes**.
   a) For 0°, place the tubes (1A and 1B) in an ice bath.
   b) For room temperature leave the tubes (2A and 2B) in the rack at the group's work area.
      Determine what room temperature is today and record this information on the chart above.
   c) For 37°, place the tubes (3A and 3B) in a 37° water bath.
   d) For 100°, place the enzyme/buffer tube (4A) in a boiling water bath.
      **Leave the sugar tube (4B) in the test tube rack at the table until step 7d below.
7) After this five minute incubation, pour the contents of each of the sucrose tubes (including tube 4B) into the corresponding enzyme buffer tubes for all four temperature conditions, as follows:
   a) Pour the contents of tube 1B into tube 1A.
   b) Pour the contents of tube 2B into tube 2A.
   c) Pour the contents of tube 3B into tube 3A.
   d) Pour the contents of tube 4B into tube 4A.
8) LEAVE THE ENZYME/BUFFER/SUCROSE TUBES AT THEIR APPROPRIATE TEMPERATURES TO INCUBATE FOR AN ADDITIONAL 5 MINUTES.
9) Toward the end of the incubation time, add 10 drops of distilled water to the 4 short test tubes.

4

62

10) Once the incubation time ends, add 5 drops from tall tube 1B to short tube 1 and mix. Be sure to use a separate dropper for each of the 4 reaction tubes.
11) Repeat Step 10 for all the corresponding tall and short tubes, that is, 5 drops from tube 2B to short tube 2 and so on until all short tubes have reaction mixture added to the distilled water.
12) Add a Clinitest™ tablet to each short tube and swirl gently to mix. **BE CAREFUL**, as the contents of the tube will get hot, heating the tube itself.
13) Record the amount of activity (Results) in the table above and at the end of the report.
14) Consult with your teammates to form a conclusion that you will record at the end of the report.

5

Exercise I: Effect of Concentration on Enzyme Activity

1) What do you predict, or hypothesize, will happen as you increase enzyme concentration?

_____

2) What results did you obtain after performing this experiment?

_____

3) What can you conclude from performing this experiment regarding the effect of concentration on enzyme activity?

_____

_____

Exercise II: Effect of pH on Enzyme Activity

1) What do you predict, or hypothesize, will happen as you change the pH?

_____

2) What results did you obtain after performing this experiment?

_____

3) What can you conclude from performing this experiment regarding the effect of pH on enzyme activity?

_____

_____

Exercise III: Effect of Temperature on Enzyme Activity

1) What do you predict, or hypothesize, will happen as you increase temperature?

_____

2) What results did you obtain after performing this experiment?

_____

3) What can you conclude from performing this experiment regarding the effect of temperature on enzyme activity?

_____

_____

POST-LAB QUESTIONS

1. Which is the name of the enzyme that breaks down sucrose into glucose and fructose? __
   a) fructase   b) sucrase   c) lactase   d) gelatinase

2. Where do you find an active site? _____
   a) in a substrate   b) in an enzyme   c) in a test tube   d) at a lively party

3. When an enzyme is denatured, it can _____.
   a) act on more than one substrate   b) act only weakly
   c) no longer act on its substrate   d) act at a different pH

4. What is the optimal temperature for an enzyme acting within the human digestive system?
   a) 0°C   b) 100°C   c) 37°C   d) 20°C

5. Which of the following is not an enzyme?
   a) collagenase   b) urease   c) adenine   d) acetylcholinesterase

6. How did you decide that your choice for Question 5 is NOT an enzyme?

_____

7. If enzymes like sucrase are denatured at very high temperatures, how do you explain the activities of organisms that live in the deep thermal vents of the ocean, where temperatures exceed 80°C?

_____

8. If the pH of your mouth is about pH 7 and the pH of your stomach is about pH 2, what happens to the enzymes that begin working in your mouth once the food reaches your stomach? Explain.

_____

9. You're working with an enzyme that has on optimal pH of 6.5.
   a) What happens to the activity of this enzyme when the pH is **lower** than 6.5? _____
   b) What happens to the activity of this enzyme when the pH is **higher** than 6.5? _____
   Draw the graph of the activity of this enzyme in the area below.

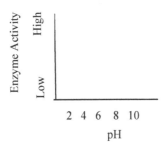

7

10. When a person has a high fever, their cellular activities may be abnormal. Based on your understanding of enzyme activity, explain what makes this happen.

_____

_____

11. Sometimes drowning victims submerged in cold water survive prolonged periods of being under water. How would you explain this, based on your knowledge of enzymes?

_____

_____

LAB: ENZYME ACTIVITY II

Enzymes enable many chemical reactions to proceed more rapidly than they might otherwise do. Some help bring the substances in cells together to form larger molecules; others break larger molecules into smaller ones. The addition of **"ase"** onto the end of a word in biology tells you that the word is the name of an enzyme. For example, sucrase is the enzyme that breaks down the disaccharide sucrose into the monosaccharides glucose and fructose.

Because nearly all **enzymes** are proteins they behave like proteins do. As a result of the order of amino acids forming the primary structure of the protein, every enzyme has a particular shape, its tertiary structure. This shape contains an **active site**, a sort of groove or "pocket" where the **substrate**, the material on which the enzyme acts, fits so the reaction can take place. Consider the active site to be a lock, such as that in your car door, and the substrate to be the key that fits into that particular lock and no other. Anything that changes the shape of this active site alters the way in which the enzyme works, possibly preventing enzyme activity altogether. Such changes include exposure to extreme heat or extremes of pH, either very acidic or very basic environments. All of these conditions can cause a drastic change in the shape of the enzyme; this change is called **denaturation**. Once an enzyme is denatured it cannot return to its original shape and thus cannot perform its function. In fact, this is one reason we cook some of our food, to destroy any microorganisms present by destroying their enzyme function. Denaturing the protein of the meat we eat makes it both tastier and easier to chew. Some foods can actually be "cooked" by soaking them in an acidic substance; a dish called seviche is made by marinating scallops in lime or lemon juice for several hours, giving it a texture identical to what it would have if it were poached in wine or sautéed in butter.

In today's lab, you will work as part of a team, each group examining a particular aspect of enzyme activity, using an enzyme called **amylase** whose function is to catalyze the breakdown of sugar and starch. Amylase breaks down polysaccharides into smaller disaccharide subunits and finally to monosaccharides, glucose being an example. In humans, the main amylases present are salivary amylase (made by the salivary glands) and pancreatic amylase that is made in and secreted by the pancreas. The primary function of these enzymes is to break down starches present in some of the foods we eat so that they can be used by the body. People who can't digest fats (fat intolerant) will often increase their intake of carbohydrates to help make up for the lack of fat intake in their diet. In addition to digesting carbohydrates, amylase will also digest dead white blood cells, the primary component of pus.

One group will look at the effect that the amount, or concentration, of enzyme has on overall activity. Another group will explore the effect of different pH levels on enzyme activity. A third group will test the effect of various temperatures on the enzyme activity.

Before separating into groups, your instructor may ask for some volunteers to help demonstrate the assay that will be used to determine the extent of enzyme activity under each condition to be tested. The basic reaction is:

$$\text{Starch} \xrightarrow{\text{Amylase}} \rightarrow \quad \text{disaccharides} \quad + \quad \text{monoscaccharides}$$
$$\text{(maltose)} \qquad\qquad \text{(glucose)}$$

In order to determine whether a reaction has taken place, you will test for the formation of simple sugars (monosaccharides) by adding Benedict's solution to a test tube, boiling the tube and its contents and watching for a color change to take place. **BE CAREFUL**, as the contents of the tube will get hot. The contents of a test tube that has a monosaccharide will change color. The color will be dependent on the concentration of glucose formed from the digestion of the starch as noted in the following table. If no monosaccharide is present, the contents will remain a light blue color. This indicates that no enzyme activity has occurred.

Color reaction	Amount of glucose present
Light blue	No glucose present
Light Green	Very low levels present
Yellow	Low levels present
Yellow-Orange	Moderate levels present
Orange	High levels present
Red	Very high levels present

Before beginning their experiments, members of Groups I, II and III need to practice using the glass pipette and rubber bulb to deliver liquids required in this lab. Your instructor will demonstrate the use of these pieces of equipment. Practice with a glass beaker and tap water. The pipette is marked off in milliliter divisions. When filled to the upper line, the pipette would contain its maximum volume; for example, a 5 ml pipette holds 5 ml when filled to the top line. When filled to the largest line below this top line, it contains 4 ml and so on. The bulb has a large center ball which, when squeezed, generates suction to obtain the necessary liquid. The bulb also has three small "bubbles" each of which has a letter, as follows: the top one has an "A", the middle one an "S" and the side one an "E". Squeeze the "A" button and the large ball to deflate the large ball, then carefully place the non-pointed end of the pipette in the hole at the bottom of the rubber bulb and insert the pointed end of the pipette into the beaker of water. Squeeze the "S" button until the correct amount of liquid is obtained. To empty the contents of the pipette, squeeze the "E" button to expel the liquid into the appropriate container. Avoid pulling liquid into the large ball as it ruins the pipette bulb. Practice this activity until you feel comfortable measuring liquids this way. You may use the same pipette to deliver the same solution into different test tubes, but **make sure to use a clean pipette for each different solution**. When you're finished with all your pipetting tasks, squeeze the "A" button to re-inflate the large ball.

When you have completed the experiment, you will record your team's results, develop a **one sentence** conclusion that explains these results and appoint a spokesperson to stand in the front of the room and orally share these results and this conclusion with the rest of class.

I.   Effect of Enzyme Concentration on Enzyme Activity

Your group will be examining how the amount or concentration of enzyme affects the rate of enzyme activity in a reaction. Set up the six tall test tubes according to the chart below:

Table I   Enzyme Concentration Set-Up

Tube #	mL enzyme	mL H$_2$O	mL pH 8.0 buffer	mL starch	Enzyme concentration	Enzyme activity
1	1.00	1.00	2.50	None	100%	
2	1.00	None	2.50	1.00	100%	
3	0.50	None	2.50	1.00	50%	
4	0.25	None	2.50	1.00	20%	
5	0.10	None	2.50	1.00	10%	

Mix enzyme, H$_2$O and buffer as indicated for each tube. After all the tubes are set up, initiate the reaction by adding 1.0 ml of the starch solution to each tube except tube #1. Place the tubes in the test tube rack in the 37C water bath to incubate for 10 minutes. Toward the end of the incubation time, add 7 drops of Benedict's solution to each tube, gentle mix and place in boiling water bath for 10 minutes. Remove tubes (**BE CAREFUL**), as the contents of the tube are hot. Record the amount of enzyme activity in the table above and consult with your teammates to form a conclusion that you will present to the class.

CONCLUSION STATEMENT: _____
_____

II.   Effect of pH on Enzyme Activity

Your group will be examining how the pH of the environment affects the rate of enzyme activity in a reaction. Each enzyme operates best at an **optimal** pH.   Set up the 4 tall test tubes according to the chart below:

Table II pH Exercise Set-Up

Tube #	mL enzyme	mL buffer	mL starch	Enzyme activity
1	0.500	2.50 pH 1.0	1.00	
2	0.500	2.50 pH 4.4	1.00	
3	0.500	2.50 pH 8.0	1.00	
4	0.500	2.50 pH 12.0	1.00	

Mix enzyme, and buffer as indicated for each tube. After mixing, add 1 ml of starch to each tube and let the tubes sit in the test tube rack in the 37C water bath to incubate for 10 minutes. Toward the end of the incubation time, add 7 drops of Benedict's Solution to each tube, gently mix and place tubes in a boiling water bath for 10 minutes. **BE CAREFUL**, as the contents of the tube will get hot. Record the amount of enzyme activity in the table above and consult with your teammates to form a conclusion that you will present to the class.

CONCLUSION STATEMENT: _____

_____

III. Effect of Temperature on Enzyme Activity

Your group will be examining how the temperature of the environment affects the rate of enzyme activity in a reaction. Each enzyme operates best at an **optimal** temperature. You will be setting up 8 test tubes, 4 with enzyme and buffer and 4 with just starch. Mark them clearly! Set up the tall test tubes according to the chart below:

Table III   Temperature Exercise Set-Up

Tube #	mL enzyme	mL pH 8.0 buffer	mL starch	Temperature (degrees C)	Enzyme activity
1A	0.50	2.50	none	$0°$	
2A	0.50	2.50	1none	___ $°$ (room temperature)	
3A	0.50	2.50	1none	$37°$	
4A	0.50	2.50	1none	$100°$	
1B	none	none	1.0	$0°$	
2B	none	none	1.0	___ $°$ (room temperature)	
3B	none	none	1.0	$37°$	
4B	none	none	1.0	$100°$	

Mix enzyme and buffer in tubes 1A, 2A, 3A and 4A. Incubate these enzyme/buffer tubes at their appropriate temperatures for 5 minutes. The tubes at $0°$ will be placed in an ice bath. The tubes at room temperature (determine what this is today) will be left in the rack at the group's work area. The tubes at $37°$ will be placed in a $37°$ water bath and the tubes at $100°$ will be placed in a boiling water bath. For tubes 1B, 2B, and 3B and 4B add 1.0 ml starch, place at their appropriate temperatures.

After this first five minutes, add the 1.0 ml of starch solution to each of the tubes for all four temperature conditions and LEAVE THE ENZYME/BUFFER/STARCH TUBES AT THEIR APPROPRIATE TEMPERATURES. Incubate for an additional 10 minutes. Toward the end of the incubation time, add 7 drops of Benedict's Solution to each test tube and swirl gently to mix. Place test tubes in boiling water bath for 10 minutes. **BE CAREFUL**, as the contents of the tube will get hot. Record the amount of enzyme activity in the table above and consult with your teammates to form a conclusion that you will present to the class.

CONCLUSION STATEMENT: _____

_____

POST-LAB QUESTIONS

1. Which is the enzyme that breaks down starch into glucose? _____
   a) fructase   b) gelatinase   c) lactase   d) amylase

2. Where do you find an active site? _____
   a) in a substrate   b) in an enzyme   c) in a test tube   d) at a lively party

3. When an enzyme is denatured, it can _____.
   a) act on more than one substrate   b) act only weakly   c) no longer act on its substrate
   d) act at a different pH

4. What is the optimal temperature for an enzyme acting within the human digestive system?
   a) $0°C$ b) $100°C$ c) $37°C$ d) $20°C$

5. Which of the following is not an enzyme? How can you tell?
   a) collagenase   b) urease   c) adenine   d) acetylcholinesterase

_____

6. If enzymes like sucrase are denatured at very high temperatures, how do you explain the activities of organisms that live in the deep thermal vents of the ocean, where temperatures exceed $80°C$?

_____

7. If the pH of your mouth is about pH 7 and the pH of your stomach is about pH 2, what happens to the activity of enzymes that begin working in your mouth when the food reaches your stomach? Explain. _____

8. You're working with an enzyme that has on optimal pH of 6.5.
   What is true of the activity of this enzyme when the pH is lower than 6.5? _____
   What is true of the activity of this enzyme when the pH is higher than 6.5? _____
   Draw the graph of this in the area below.

9. When a person has a high fever, their cellular activities may be abnormal. Based on your understanding of enzyme activity, explain what makes this happen.

_____

_____

10. Sometimes drowning victims submerged in cold water survive prolonged periods of being under water. How would you explain this, based on your knowledge of enzymes? _____

_____

Class Activity: CELLULAR RESPIRATION/PHOTOSYNTHESIS

1. Work in small groups.
2. Add 60 ml of tap water to two 150 ml beakers.
3. Next add 2 ml of a Bromthymol Blue stock solution (stock =0.04% BTB in water) to each beaker and mix. The resulting color should be a dark blue or dark blue-green.
4. Place a clean straw into each beaker.
5. One member of the group should rest for several minutes (no movement or exertion on their part). Another group member will act as the timer.
6. When the timer gives the word, the resting student should slowly blow air through the straw into the bottom of the solution in beaker 1. The student is not to inhale during the process.
7. When the solution changes from a blue to a yellow color, the timer should indicate **"STOP"** to the student blowing through the straw. The time that elapsed for the solution to change color should be recorded. Next the same student should exercise for several minutes (running in place for example). Repeat steps 6 and 7 using the second beaker. Again the time that elapsed for the second solution to change color should be recorded.

Time for beaker 1 color change:	Time for beaker 2 color change:

EXPLAIN YOUR RESULTS:
- **What gases are found in exhaled air?**
- **Why is there a difference between the two beakers?**
- **How is this experiment related to CELLULAR RESPIRATION?**

8. From the previous experiment, take a beaker that has the solution that has changed color and divide the contents equally between two beakers.
9. To one beaker, submerge a healthy sprig of an aquatic plant such as *Anarchis* or *Elodea*.
10. Place both beakers under a light for about an hour and observe the color of each solution.

Color change for beaker with sprig:	Color change for beaker without sprig:

EXPLAIN YOUR RESULTS:
- **Why is there a difference between the two beakers?**
- **How is this experiment related to PHOTOSYNTHESIS?**

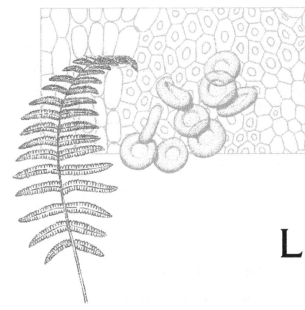

Lab: Photosynthesis

I. Measuring the Effects of Different Variables on the Rate of Photosynthesis:

$$\underset{\text{Carbon Dioxide}}{6\,CO_2} + \underset{\text{Water}}{6\,H_2O} \xrightarrow{\text{Light Energy}} \underset{\text{Glucose}}{C_6H_{12}O_6} + \underset{\text{Oxygen}}{6\,O_2} \rightarrow \rightarrow \rightarrow \underset{\text{(Plants \& Some Protists)}}{STARCH}$$

Photosynthesis is a biosynthetic, endergonic (energy-requiring) chemical reaction that occurs in plants, some protists and some bacteria. Like all chemical reactions occurring in living organisms, it is catalyzed by specific enzymes and is, therefore, affected by conditions that alter the activity of enzymes.

What variables having to do with light energy might have an effect on the rate of photosynthesis?

_____

_____

How might temperature affect the rate?

_____

_____

What other variables might affect the rate?

_____

_____

In this exercise you will use an assay called the **Floating Leaf Disk Assay**, to measure the relative rates of photosynthesis. As leaf disks photosynthesize, they produce oxygen gas (one of the products of photosynthesis). When enough oxygen gas has accumulated, the leaf disks will float to the surface of a water solution. The time it takes for the disks to float to the surface provides an indirect measurement of the rate of photosynthesis occurring in the disks. In part I of this exercise you will use the leaf disk assay to measure the effects of $NaHCO_3$, sodium bicarbonate, on the rate of photosynthesis. Sodium bicarbonate is a source of carbon dioxide. In part II, you will design your own experiment to measure the effects of one of the variables you listed above.

Part I:

Materials:

25mL syringe	**Forceps**	**Buffer B ($NaHCO_3$)**
Paper punch	**Rubber syringe seal**	**Fluorescent light source**
Buffer A (no $NaHCO_3$)	**Petri dishes**	**Small beakers**
Green spinach leaves		

1. Obtain several green spinach leaves and, using the paper punch, punch out 20 leaf disks. Place the disks in a Petri dish containing a small amount of Buffer A.

2. Pull out the plunger of a 25mL syringe and, using forceps, transfer 10 leaf disks into the syringe. Replace the plunger, but **be careful not** to crush the leaf disks.

3. Pour about 20mL of Buffer A into a small beaker. Use this solution to draw 15mL of Buffer A into the syringe containing the leaf disks. Invert the syringe and gently push the plunger to remove any air.

4. Press the rubber syringe seal tightly over the syringe tip and pull back on the plunger. This will create a vacuum that will pull gases out of the leaf disks and allow them to sink to the bottom of the syringe.

5. Set up a fluorescent light source. Stand the syringe (tip facing up) about 5cm from the light. Record the time it takes for the first and last leaf disks to reach the top of the syringe.

6. Repeat this procedure using 10 new leaf disks and 15mL of Buffer B.

What is the variable being tested in this experiment?

_____

_____

What would you predict will be different when you use Buffer B instead of Buffer A? Why?

_____

_____

Part II:

For the Floating Leaf Disk Assay experiment in Part I complete the sections below:

State the problem, hypothesis, independent variable and dependent variable:

_____

_____

_____

_____

_____

_____

The Results and Conclusion:

_____

_____

_____

_____

_____

_____

_____

_____

_____

_____

_____

_____

_____

_____

_____

_____

_____

_____

_____

_____

_____

_____

_____

_____

_____

_____

_____

_____

II. Light and Photosynthesis:

In this exercise a healthy geranium plant was placed in darkness for 48 hours. Some leaves were then masked with black construction paper and the plant was exposed to sunlight for 24 hours. You will test a masked leaf for the distribution of starch. Starch will react with iodine to produce a black color. (See figure 3. in the first photosynthesis lab in this manual.)

1. Remove a masked leaf from the geranium plant. Note the position of the mask or trace the leaf on paper, showing the position of the mask.

2. Place the leaf in boiling water for 3-5 minutes.

3. Transfer the leaf to boiling alcohol. Boil the leaf until the chlorophyll has been extracted.

4. Place the leaf in a Petri dish and completely cover it with iodine solution for 3 minutes. Rinse with water and examine it.

Explain the results of this experiment in terms of photosynthesis.

III. Separation of Plant Pigments by Paper Chromatography:

In the first photosynthesis lab in this manual, you used paper chromatography to separate the plant pigments, chlorophyll a, chlorophyll b, xanthophyll and beta-carotene. In this exercise you will predict the results of the separation of these pigments using your knowledge of the properties of polar and nonpolar molecules.

The following information will help you make your prediction:

1. Polar molecules are attracted to (dissolve in) other polar molecules and repelled by nonpolar molecules.

2. Nonpolar molecules are attracted to other nonpolar molecules and repelled by polar molecules.

3. Chromatography paper is made up of cellulose, a polar molecule.

4. The chromatography solvent used for plant pigment separation is nonpolar.

5. The most nonpolar pigment will dissolve in the solvent first.

6. The most polar pigment will be strongly attracted to the paper (cellulose) move last.

Using the structural formulas in figure1. below, determine the number of polar groups in each of the four plant pigments:

Chlorophyll a: _____ polar groups

Chlorophyll b: _____ polar groups

Xanthophyll: _____ polar groups

Beta-carotene: _____ polar groups

Molecular structure of major leaf pigments. The molecular structure of chlorophyll a, chlorophyll b, beta-carotene, and xanthophyll. Count the number of polar groups present in each molecule. Polar groups include CHO, O, CO, and OCH₃.

(a) Chlorophyll a

(b) Chlorophyll b

(c) Beta-carotene

(d) Xanthophyll

Based on the polarity of these molecules, predict the separation pattern of the plant pigments:

Pigment closest to the top of the chromatography paper: _____

Second from the top: _____

Third from the top: _____

Bottom of paper: _____

Assignment: Create a Protein

Name: _____ Due: _____

There is a gene in the DNA molecule of a human that codes for an enzyme needed for melanin (skin pigment molecule) production. Using your knowledge of protein synthesis, determine the nucleotide sequence in the mRNA molecule (TRANSCRIPTION) and the amino acid sequence in the protein coded for by the DNA gene (TRANSLATION):

DNA: **TAC AGA GGC TTT ACT**

mRNA:

Protein:

A mutation has been detected in the DNA molecule of one individual in the population, the fourth nucleotide from the left has been changed from A to G. What change in the protein will occur?

DNA: TAC **G**GA GGC TTT ACT

mRNA:

Protein

What effect will this change have on the organism or its offspring if the mutation is in a skin cell (be specific; remember this gene is needed for melanin production)?

What effect will this change have on the organism or its offspring if the mutation is in a germ cell (be specific; remember this gene is needed for melanin production)?

Class Activity: Human Reproduction on the Cellular Level

Name:_____

Assignment: Mitosis-Meiosis Video

Name: _____ Due: _____

PART 1:

    1.) _____

    2.) _____

    3.) _____

    4.) _____

    5.) _____

PART 2:

    1.) _____

    2.) _____

    3.) _____

    4.) _____

    5.) _____

LAB: MITOSIS and MEIOSIS

Demonstrate how the phases of mitosis and meiosis differ by drawing the arrangement of chromosomes for an organism having the diploid (2n) number of 4. Pipe cleaner models of the chromosomes may be used to help with this activity.

MITOSIS:

Metaphase: **Anaphase:**

MEIOSIS:

Metaphase I: **Anaphase I:**

Metaphase II: **Anaphase II:**

ASSIGNMENT: GENETICS

Name: _____   Due: _____

The species, _____ **has the following phenotype varieties:**

- **Body color: Blue or Pink**

- **Hair: Wavy or Straight**

- **Finger number: 4 or 5**

- **Head width: Wide or Narrow**

1. Mr. Mariner is the Mitchell College Mascot. He has the following genotypes for **body color, hair, finger number**, and **head width** respectively: Bb, WW, ff, Hh. For each of his genotypes, indicate whether it is **heterozygous** or **homozygous**.

Bb: _____   WW: _____

ff: _____   Hh: _____

2. In Mr. Mariner's family, a blue body color (B) is dominant to pink (b). Determine the phenotype for each genotype below based on this information.

BB _____   Bb _____   bb _____

3. If wide heads (H) are dominant to narrow heads (h), give the genotypes that are possible for the species *Mascot marinus.*

Wide Head: _____   Narrow Head: _____

4. Mr. Mariner has 4 fingers. The 4 finger trait is coded for by a recessive allele (f). If Mrs. Mariner has 5 fingers (F) and is heterozygous for this trait how many fingers will their children have?

    A. List the genotypes for Mr. and Mrs. Mariner:

    Mr. Mariner: _____   Mrs. Mariner: _____

    B. Complete the Punnett square to show the possibilities that would

    result for their children.

    C. List the possible genotypes and phenotypes for their children.

    Genotypes: _____

    Phenotypes: _____

    D. What are the chances a child will have 4 fingers? _____%

    E. What are the chances a child will have 5 fingers? _____%

5. Mr. Mariner is homozygous for his wavy hair; an important feature for his position as the Mitchell College Mascot! Wavy hair is coded for by a dominant allele (W). Mrs. Mariner has the recessive trait of straight hair (w). Will any of their children be able to take over as the Mitchell College Mascot when Mr. Mariner retires???

    A. List the genotypes for Mr. and Mrs. Mariner:

    Mr. Mariner: _____   Mrs. Mariner: _____

    B. Complete the Punnett square to show the possibilities that would

    result for their children.

    C. List the possible genotypes and phenotypes for their children.

    Genotypes: _____

    Phenotypes: _____

    D. What are the chances a child will have wavy hair? _____%

    E. What are the chances a child will have straight hair? _____%

Assignment: Miracle of Life Video

Name: _____ Due: _____

1.) All humans begin as a single cell (Zygote). How many cells are in a typical human?

2.) How many sperm are produced per day by a typical human male?

3.) How many sperm are released with each ejaculation?

4.) Name 2 reasons why most sperm released will not make it to the egg (ovum)?

5.) What creates identical twins?

6.) Can the sex of a 7 week old embryo be determined by examination?

7.) When all of the major organs are in place, the embryo becomes a fetus. At what age of the embryo does this occur?

8.) Why can't a fetus hear before the fifth month of development?

9.) What does the contraction of the uterus do to prepare the woman's body for childbirth?

10.) Why is human birth much more dangerous than the birth of other mammals?

Lab: Fetal Pig Dissection

You will work in groups to identify the following structures in a fetal pig. Once you are sure you have located the structures listed below, have your instructor check your work.

- o Epiglottis

- o Hard and soft palates

- o Pharynx

- o Esophagus

- o Diaphragm

- o Lungs

- o Heart

- o Larynx

- o Trachea

- o Stomach

- o Spleen

- o Small Intestine

- o Pancreas

- o Liver

- o Gall bladder

- o Cecum

- o Large intestine (colon)

- o Rectum

- o Anus

ASSIGNMENT:NUTRITIONAL ANALYSIS

This is an **individual** assignment that will be part of your **final exam** for BI143. This assignment is due on:_____. Since it is part of your final exam, **NO LATE** assignments will be accepted.

The Assignment:

1.) You will keep a journal of the foods and beverages (except water, or zero-calorie drinks), that you consume for 2 days. For the first day you will eat whatever you like. On the second day you will try to eat a healthier diet based on your nutritional analysis of the first day. You will complete a nutritional analysis of the second day for comparison. Use the form provided to for your journal and analysis. Additional forms can be found on your instructor's webpage.

2.) To complete the nutritional analysis you will visit **www.nutritiondata.com,** the sodexo nutrition website (http://www.yourhealthyourwayonline.com/calc_frameset.htm) and you will use the attached DQS chart.

   a. First, you will calculate your BMI and Daily Nutritional Needs. Record your daily requirements for:

      i. Calories
      ii. Protein in grams (g)
      iii. Carbohydrates in grams (g)
      iv. Fat (g)
         Use the following information to approximate your daily requirement for fats:
         A 1,600 calorie per day diet: 53 grams of fat or less
         A 2,000 calorie per day diet: 65 grams of fat or less
         A 2,200 calorie per day diet: 73 grams of fat or less
         A 2,500 calorie per day diet: 80 grams of fat or less
         A 2,800 calorie per day diet: 93 grams of fat or less

3.) On Day 1, eat as you normally would. Each time you eat or drink something, track its point score in the space provided. Be sure to write down a description of the food that you ate. If it's your first serving of that particular type of food or drink that day, use the DQS score in the 1st column. If it's your second serving of that particular type of food or drink that day, use the DQS score in the 2nd column, and so forth. Start with breakfast and keep a running tally throughout the day. After your last meal, snack or drink before bedtime, note your total DQS for the day. Using the Nutritiondata.com website, identify the amount of protein, carbohydrate, and fat you ingested for each day. Compare these amounts to the ideal amount of protein, carbohydrate and fat that you should be taking in each day.

4.) On Day 2, try to improve your score as much as possible. Avoid those foods that will earn you negative points, while attempting to eat as many of the "positive" foods as possible. Track and record your food as you did on Day 1. Again, using the Nutritiondata.com website, identify the amount of protein, carbohydrate, and fat you ingested for each day. Compare these amounts to the ideal amount of protein, carbohydrate and fat that you should be taking in each day.

    a. Third, you will complete the analysis comparing your diet to your nutritional needs.

5.) Your graded journal will be returned to you the week of April 26 along with questions to answer. The answers to these questions will be due the day of your scheduled final exam for BI143.

6.) This entire assignment must be typed or VERY neatly handwritten.

7.) **REMEMBER:** This is an individual assignment. Plagiarism will result in a final exam grade of zero.

Diet Quality Score Table:

Nutrition scientists have come up with various ways of measuring diet quality. The table on this page is an extremely simplified version of these more complicated methods. The highest score that you can get on any given day is 32 points. Don't be surprised if you have a negative score the first time that you do this! Many people do. You'll see that it is much easier than you think to get your score in the positive range. The key is to pay attention.

Diet Quality Score
(DQS)

	1st	2nd	3rd	4th	5th	6th	
Fruit	2	2	2	1	0	0	0
Vegetable	2	2	2	1	0	0	0
Lean Protein	2	2	1	0	0	0	0
Whole Grain	2	2	1	0	0	0	0
Low-Fat Dairy	1	1	1	0	0	0	0
Omega-3 Fats	2	0	0	0	0	0	0
Refined Grain	-1	-1	-2	-2	-2	-2	
Sweet	-2	-2	-2	-2	-2	-2	
Fried Food	-2	-2	-2	-2	-2	-2	
Full Fat Dairy	-1	-1	-2	-2	-2	-2	
Fatty Protein	-1	-1	-2	-2	-2	-2	

Fruit	1 apple, 1 banana, 1 pear, 1 orange, etc.
	1 handful of berries, grapes, etc.
	8 oz 100% fruit juice
Vegetable	1/2 cup cooked vegetables
	1 cup salad
	fist sized portion raw vegetables (broccoli, carrots)
Lean Protein	Open-hand portion meat, fish or tofu
	1 egg or 2 egg whites
	handful of nuts
Whole Grain	1-2 slices whole grain bread
	1 cup whole grain breakfast cereal
	whole grain pasta
	fist sized portion brown rice, etc
Low-Fat Dairy	8 oz skim milk
	2 slices low fat cheese
	8 oz low fat yogurt
Omega-3 Fats	Open-hand portion wild (not farmed) salmon
	1/4 cup ground flax seeds
	1/4 cup almonds
	1 serving fish oil

Day 1

Food/Beverage Description	DQS Points	Protein	Carb	Fat	Calories
TOTAL					
IDEAL					

DAY 2

Food/Beverage Description	DQS Points	Protein	Carb	Fat	Calories
TOTAL					
IDEAL					

LEXICON: Chapter 1

Name: _____ Due: _____

Please neatly WRITE the definitions of the following terms:

Animal

_____
_____
_____
_____

Archaea

_____
_____
_____
_____

Bacteria

_____
_____
_____
_____

Biology

_____
_____
_____
_____

Biosphere

_____
_____
_____
_____

Cell

_____

_____

_____

_____

Community

_____

_____

_____

_____

Consumer

_____

_____

_____

_____

Controlled Experiment

_____

_____

_____

_____

Decomposer

_____

_____

_____

_____

Dependent Variable

_____

_____

_____

_____

Domain

_____
_____
_____
_____

Ecosystem

_____
_____
_____
_____

Eukarya

_____
_____
_____
_____

Evolution

_____
_____
_____
_____

Fungus

_____
_____
_____
_____

Genus

_____
_____
_____
_____

Hypothesis

_____
_____
_____
_____

Independent Variable

_____
_____
_____
_____

Kingdom

_____
_____
_____
_____

Natural Selection

_____
_____
_____
_____

Organ

_____
_____
_____
_____

Organism

_____
_____
_____
_____

Organelle

_____
_____
_____
_____

Organ System

_____
_____
_____
_____

Plant

_____
_____
_____
_____

Population

_____
_____
_____
_____

Producer

_____
_____
_____
_____

Protist

_____
_____
_____
_____

Scientific Method

_____
_____
_____
_____

Species

_____
_____
_____
_____

Theory

_____
_____
_____
_____

Name: _____ Due: _____

Please neatly WRITE the definitions of the following terms:

Abiotic synthesis

_____
_____
_____
_____

Archaea

_____
_____
_____
_____

Autotroph

_____
_____
_____
_____

Bacteria

_____
_____
_____
_____

Biogenesis

_____
_____
_____
_____

Chloroplasts

_____

_____

_____

_____

Endosymbiosis

_____

_____

_____

_____

Extreme Halophile

_____

_____

_____

_____

Extreme Thermophile

_____

_____

_____

_____

Eukaryotes

_____

_____

_____

_____

Heterotroph

_____

_____

_____

_____

Mitochondria

_____
_____
_____
_____

Prokaryotes

_____
_____
_____
_____

Protobiont

_____
_____
_____
_____

Spontaneous Generation

_____
_____
_____
_____

Name: _____ Due: _____

Please neatly WRITE the definitions of the following terms:

Acid

_____
_____
_____
_____

Acid Precipitation

_____
_____
_____
_____

Atom

_____
_____
_____
_____

Atomic Mass

_____
_____
_____
_____

Atomic Number

_____
_____
_____
_____

Base

_____

_____

_____

_____

Buffer

_____

_____

_____

_____

Chemical Bond

_____

_____

_____

_____

Compound

_____

_____

_____

_____

Electron

_____

_____

_____

_____

Electron Shell (Orbit)

_____

_____

_____

_____

Element

_____

_____

_____

_____

Ion

_____

_____

_____

_____

Ionic Compound

_____

_____

_____

_____

Matter

_____

_____

_____

_____

Molecule

_____

_____

_____

_____

Molecular Compound

_____

_____

_____

_____

Neutron

_____
_____
_____
_____

Nonpolar Molecule

_____
_____
_____
_____

pH Scale

_____
_____
_____
_____

Polar Molecule

_____
_____
_____
_____

Proton

_____
_____
_____
_____

Solution

_____
_____
_____
_____

LEXICON: Chapter 3

Name: _____ Due: _____

Please neatly WRITE the definitions of the following terms:

Amino Acid

_____

_____

_____

_____

Carbohydrate

_____

_____

_____

_____

Cellulose

_____

_____

_____

_____

Dehydration Synthesis

_____

_____

_____

_____

Denaturation

_____

_____

_____

_____

Deoxyribonucleic Acid (DNA)

_____
_____
_____
_____

Double Helix

_____
_____
_____
_____

Enzyme

_____
_____
_____
_____

Fat (Triglyceride)

_____
_____
_____
_____

Glycogen

_____
_____
_____
_____

Hydrolysis

_____
_____
_____
_____

Hydrophilic

_____
_____
_____
_____

Hydrophobic

_____
_____
_____
_____

Lipid

_____
_____
_____
_____

Macromolecule

_____
_____
_____
_____

Monomer

_____
_____
_____
_____

Monosaccharide

_____

_____

_____

_____

Nucleic Acid

_____

_____

_____

_____

Nucleotide

_____

_____

_____

_____

Phospholipids

_____

_____

_____

_____

Polymer

_____

_____

_____

_____

Polypeptide

_____

_____

_____

_____

Polysaccharide

_____

_____

_____

_____

Primary Structure

_____

_____

_____

_____

Protein

_____

_____

_____

_____

Quaternary Structure

_____

_____

_____

_____

Ribonucleic Acid (RNA)

_____

_____

_____

_____

Secondary Structure

_____

_____

_____

_____

Starch

_____
_____
_____
_____

Tertiary Structure

_____
_____
_____
_____

LEXICON: Chapter 4

Name: _____ Due: _____

Please neatly WRITE the definitions of the following terms:

Cell Theory

_____

_____

_____

_____

Cell Wall

_____

_____

_____

_____

Cellular Metabolism

_____

_____

_____

_____

Central Vacuole

_____

_____

_____

_____

Centriole

_____

_____

_____

_____

Chloroplast

_____

_____

_____

_____

Chromatin

_____

_____

_____

_____

Chromosome

_____

_____

_____

_____

Cilia

_____

_____

_____

_____

Cytoplasm

_____

_____

_____

_____

Cytoskeleton

_____

_____

_____

_____

Endoplasmic Reticulum

_____
_____
_____
_____

Eukaryotic Cell

_____
_____
_____
_____

Flagella

_____
_____
_____
_____

Golgi Apparatus

_____
_____
_____
_____

Lysosomes

_____
_____
_____
_____

Mitochondria

_____
_____
_____
_____

Nuclear Envelope

_____
_____
_____
_____

Nucleolus

_____
_____
_____
_____

Nucleus

_____
_____
_____
_____

Organelle

_____
_____
_____
_____

Plasma Membrane

_____
_____
_____
_____

Prokaryotic Cell

_____
_____
_____
_____

Ribosome

_____

_____

_____

_____

Transport Vesicle

_____

_____

_____

_____

Vacuole

_____

_____

_____

_____

LEXICON: Chapter 5

Name: _____ Due: _____

Please neatly WRITE the definitions of the following terms:

Phospholipid

_____
_____
_____
_____

Passive Transport

_____
_____
_____
_____

Active Transport

_____
_____
_____
_____

Diffusion

_____
_____
_____
_____

Osmosis

_____
_____
_____
_____

Facilitated Diffusion

_____

_____

_____

_____

Endocytosis

_____

_____

_____

_____

Exocytosis

_____

_____

_____

_____

Hypotonic

_____

_____

_____

_____

Hypertonic

_____

_____

_____

_____

Isotonic

_____

_____

_____

_____

Enzyme

_____
_____
_____
_____

Metabolism

_____
_____
_____
_____

Endergonic

_____
_____
_____
_____

Exergonic

_____
_____
_____
_____

Cellular Respiration

_____
_____
_____
_____

Photosynthesis

_____
_____
_____
_____

ATP

_____

_____

_____

_____

Denatured

_____

_____

_____

_____

Cofactor

_____

_____

_____

_____

Coenzyme

_____

_____

_____

_____

Active Site

_____

_____

_____

_____

LEXICON: Chapter 6

Name: _____ Due: _____

Please neatly WRITE the definitions of the following terms:

Cellular Respiration

_____
_____
_____
_____

Photosynthesis

_____
_____
_____
_____

Mitochondria

_____
_____
_____
_____

Aerobic

_____
_____
_____
_____

Anaerobic

_____
_____
_____
_____

Glycolysis

_____

_____

_____

_____

Citric Acid Cycle

_____

_____

_____

_____

Oxidative Phosphorylation

_____

_____

_____

_____

Fermentation (Lactic Acid and Alcohol)

_____

_____

_____

_____

ATP

_____

_____

_____

_____

LEXICON: Chapter 7

Name: _____ Due: _____

Please neatly WRITE the definitions of the following terms:

Photosynthesis

_____
_____
_____
_____

Chloroplast

_____
_____
_____
_____

Chlorophyll

_____
_____
_____
_____

Endergonic

_____
_____
_____
_____

Greenhouse Gases

_____
_____
_____
_____

Global Warming

_____
_____
_____
_____

Greenhouse Effect

_____
_____
_____
_____

Acid Rain

_____
_____
_____
_____

Autotrophs

_____
_____
_____
_____

Producers

_____
_____
_____
_____

LEXICON: Chapter 10

Name: _____ Due: _____

Please neatly WRITE the definitions of the following terms:

Adenine (A)

_____

_____

_____

_____

Anticodon

_____

_____

_____

_____

Cytosine (C)

_____

_____

_____

_____

DNA polymerase

_____

_____

_____

_____

DNA replication

_____

_____

_____

_____

Double helix

_____
_____
_____
_____

Genetic code

_____
_____
_____
_____

Guanine (G)

_____
_____
_____
_____

Messenger RNA (mRNA)

_____
_____
_____
_____

Mutation

_____
_____
_____
_____

Nucleotide

_____
_____
_____
_____

RNA polymerase

_____
_____
_____
_____

Start codon

_____
_____
_____
_____

Stop codon

_____
_____
_____
_____

Thymine (T)

_____
_____
_____
_____

Transcription

_____
_____
_____

Transfer RNA (tRNA)

_____
_____
_____
_____

Translation

_____

_____

_____

_____

Uracil (U)

_____

_____

_____

_____

LEXICON: Chapter 8

Name: _____ Due: _____

Please neatly WRITE the definitions of the following terms:

Sexual reproduction

_____

_____

_____

_____

Asexual reproduction

_____

_____

_____

_____

Genome

_____

_____

_____

_____

Chromosome

_____

_____

_____

_____

Cell division

_____

_____

_____

_____

Binary fission

_____

_____

_____

_____

Chromatin

_____

_____

_____

_____

Sister chromatid

_____

_____

_____

_____

Centromere

_____

_____

_____

_____

Cell cycle

_____

_____

_____

_____

Interphase

_____

_____

_____

_____

Mitosis

_____

_____

_____

_____

Cytokinesis

_____

_____

_____

_____

Prophase

_____

_____

_____

_____

Metaphase

_____

_____

_____

_____

Anaphase

_____

_____

_____

_____

Telophase

_____

_____

_____

_____

Mitotic spindle

_____

_____

_____

_____

Cleavage furrow

_____

_____

_____

_____

Cell plate

_____

_____

_____

_____

Cancer cell (carcinoma)

_____

_____

_____

_____

Homologous chromosome

_____

_____

_____

_____

Gamete

_____

_____

_____

_____

Diploid

_____

_____

_____

_____

Haploid

_____

_____

_____

_____

Fertilization

_____

_____

_____

_____

Zygote

_____

_____

_____

_____

Meiosis

_____

_____

_____

_____

Crossing over

_____

_____

_____

_____

Nondisjunction

_____
_____
_____
_____

Germ cell

_____
_____
_____
_____

Somatic cell

_____
_____
_____
_____

Ovum

_____
_____
_____
_____

Sperm

_____
_____
_____
_____

LEXICON: Chapter 9

Name: _____ Due: _____

Please neatly WRITE the definitions of the following terms:

Autosome

_____
_____
_____
_____

ABO blood groups

_____
_____
_____
_____

Allele

_____
_____
_____
_____

Codominant

_____
_____
_____
_____

Complete dominance

_____
_____
_____
_____

Cystic fibrosis

_____

_____

_____

_____

Dihybrid cross

_____

_____

_____

_____

Dominant Allele

_____

_____

_____

_____

F_1 Generation

_____

_____

_____

_____

F_2 Generation

_____

_____

_____

_____

Genotype

_____
_____
_____
_____

Hemophilia

_____
_____
_____
_____

Heterozygous

_____
_____
_____
_____

Homozygous

_____
_____
_____
_____

Huntington's disease

_____
_____
_____
_____

Hybrid

_____
_____
_____
_____

Incomplete dominance

_____

_____

_____

_____

Monohybrid cross

_____

_____

_____

_____

P Generation

_____

_____

_____

_____

Phenotype

_____

_____

_____

_____

Polygenic inheritance

_____

_____

_____

_____

Recessive allele

_____

_____

_____

_____

Red-green colorblindness

_____

_____

_____

_____

Sex chromosome

_____

_____

_____

_____

Name: _____ Due: _____

Please neatly WRITE the definitions of the following terms:

Biodiversity

_____

_____

_____

_____

Conservation Biology

_____

_____

_____

_____

Endangered Species

_____

_____

_____

_____

Global Warming

_____

_____

_____

_____

Greenhouse Gases

_____

_____

_____

_____

Habitat Alteration

_____

_____

_____

_____

Invasive Species

_____

_____

_____

_____

Overexploitation

_____

_____

_____

_____

Restoration Ecology

_____

_____

_____

_____

TEAMWORK RUBRIC

	Advanced	Intermediate	Beginning
Contributes to Team Meetings:	Helps the team move forward by articulating the merits of alternative ideas or proposals.	Offers alternative solutions or courses of action that build on to the ideas of others.	Offers new suggestions to advance the work of the group.
Facilitates the Contributions of Team Members:	Engages team members in ways that facilitate their contributions to meetings by both constructively building upon or synthesizing the contributions of others as well as noticing when someone is not participating and inviting them to engage.	Engages team members in ways that facilitate their contributions to meetings by constructively building upon or synthesizing the contributions of others.	Engages team members in ways that facilitate their contributions to meetings by restating the views of other team members and/or asking questions for clarification.
Individual Contributions Outside of Team Meetings:	Completes all assigned tasks by deadline; work accomplished is thorough, comprehensive, and advances the project. Proactively helps other team members complete their assigned tasks to a similar level of excellence.	Completes all assigned tasks by deadline; work accomplished is thorough, comprehensive, and advances the project.	Completes all assigned tasks by deadline; work accomplished advances the project.
Fosters Constructive Team Climate:	Supports a constructive team climate by doing all of the following: • Treats team members respectfully by being polite and constructive in communication. • Uses positive vocal or written tone, facial expressions, and/or body language to convey a positive attitude about the team and its work.	Supports a constructive team climate by doing any three of the following: • Treats team members respectfully by being polite and constructive in communication. • Uses positive vocal or written tone, facial expressions, and/or body language to convey a positive attitude about the team and its work.	Supports a constructive team climate by doing any two of the following: • Treats team members respectfully by being polite and constructive in communication. • Uses positive vocal or written tone, facial expressions, and/or body language to convey a positive attitude about the team and its work.

TEAMWORK RUBRIC

	• Motivates teammates by expressing confidence about the importance of the task and the team's ability to accomplish it. • Provides assistance and/or encouragement to team members.	• Motivates teammates by expressing confidence about the importance of the task and the team's ability to accomplish it. • Provides assistance and/or encouragement to team members.	• Motivates teammates by expressing confidence about the importance of the task and the team's ability to accomplish it. • Provides assistance and/or encouragement to team members.
Responds to Conflict	Addresses destructive conflict directly and constructively, helping to manage/resolve it in a way that strengthens overall team cohesiveness and future effectiveness.	Identifies and acknowledges conflict and works to resolve it.	Identifies and acknowledges conflict and works to resolve it.

TEAMWORK RUBRIC: Score 0 to 3

Self Evaluation:

Name & Group #: _____

	Score and Comments
Contributes to Team	
Facilitates the Contributions of Team Members	
Individual Contributions Outside of Team Meetings	
Fosters Constructive Team Climate	
Responds to Conflict	

Peer Evaluation:

Name: _____

	Score and Comments
Contributes to Team	
Facilitates the Contributions of Team Members	
Individual Contributions Outside of Team Meetings	
Fosters Constructive Team Climate	
Responds to Conflict	

Peer Evaluation:

Name: _____

	Score and Comments
Contributes to Team	
Facilitates the Contributions of Team Members	
Individual Contributions Outside of Team Meetings	
Fosters Constructive Team Climate	
Responds to Conflict	

Peer Evaluation:

Name: _____

	Score and Comments
Contributes to Team	
Facilitates the Contributions of Team Members	
Individual Contributions Outside of Team Meetings	
Fosters Constructive Team Climate	
Responds to Conflict